CW00422381

Other Titles of Interest

CIRCUIT
SOURCE
BOOK 2

by

R. A. Penfold

BERNARD BABANI (publishing) LTD
THE GRAMPIANS
SHEPHERDS BUSH ROAD
LONDON W6 7NF
ENGLAND

Please Note

Although every care has been taken with the production of this book to ensure that any projects, designs, modifications and/or programs, etc., contained herewith, operate in a correct and safe manner and also that all components specified are normally available in Great Britain, the Publishers and Author do not accept responsibility in any way for the failure, including fault in design, of any project, design, modification or program to work correctly or to cause damage to any other equipment that it may be connected to or used in conjunction with, or in respect of any other damage or injury that may be so caused, nor do the Publishers accept responsibility in any way for the failure to obtain specified components.

Notice is also given that if equipment that is still under warranty is modified in any way or used or connected with home-built equipment then that warranty may be void.

© 1993 BERNARD BABANI (publishing) LTD

First Published – February 1993
Reprinted – August 1997

British Library Cataloguing in Publication Data
Penfold, R. A.
Circuit Source – Book 2
I. Title
621.3815

ISBN 0 85934 322 7

Cover Design by Gregor Arthur
Printed and bound in Great Britain by Cox & Wyman Ltd, Reading

PREFACE

This book provides a number of electronic circuits which make useful "building blocks" for designers of electronic projects. It would be an exaggeration to say that any circuit for a practical application could be built up solely from "off the shelf" circuit blocks, but it is probably fair to say that the vast majority of such circuits consist mainly of standard modules. Many simple projects can be built up from standard circuit blocks, and this book should be invaluable to those who are just starting out on electronic project design. It also provides a useful reference source for more experienced circuit designers.

All the circuits are tried and tested types, not theoretical circuits which are of little practical value. Example values are given, together with advice on how to alter the values for different filter frequencies, amplifier gains, or whatever. It is only fair to point out that the way in which the circuit blocks function, and what they actually do is not explained in detail. This book is really only intended for those who have some background knowledge of electronics, and who know their astable from their regulator. On the other hand, no advanced mathematics is required in order to make use of this book.

Virtually all the circuits are concerned with some form of signal generation (oscillators, monostables, noise generators, power supplies, etc.) or with digital electronics. Refer to (BP321) Circuit Source Book 1 for circuits that process analogue signals (amplifiers, filters, triggers, voltage comparators, etc.).

R. A. Penfold

Contents

Chapter 1

OSCILLATORS

Oscillators are used in a surprisingly large number of electronic cicuits, both linear and digital. Numerous oscillator configurations are available to the circuit designer, ranging from circuits which use about three components through to complex designs which utilize dozens of components. For most purposes quite simple oscillator circuits will suffice.

555 Astables

The most common form of oscillator is almost certainly the 555 timer integrated circuit used in its standard astable mode. This configuration is shown in the circuit diagram of Figure 1.1. C2 is the timing capacitor, and it is repeatedly charged to two-thirds of the supply potential via R1 and R2, and discharged to one-third of the supply voltage by way of R2 and an internal transistor of the 555. The output waveform at pin 3 of IC1 is rectangular. The output goes high while C2 is being charged, and low when it is being discharged. The output frequency is set by the values given to R1, R2, and C2, and is given by the formula:

$$\text{Frequency} = 1.44/(R1 + 2R2)\ C2 \text{ hertz}$$

When working out 555 output frequencies remember that the timing resistance is equal to R1 plus twice R2's value, and is not simply equal to R1 plus R2. This is due to the fact that C2 charges and discharges through R2, but only charges via R1. The resistance values should be in ohms and the capacitance values in farads when making these calculations. In practice it is generally easier to work with the capacitance values in microfarads and the resistance values in megohms. The specified values give a nominal operating frequency of just over 1kHz (1021Hz). Changes to the value of C2 have an inversely proportional affect on the output frequency, as do changes to the total timing resistance. For example, changing C2 to 10n boosts the output frequency to just over 10kHz —

1

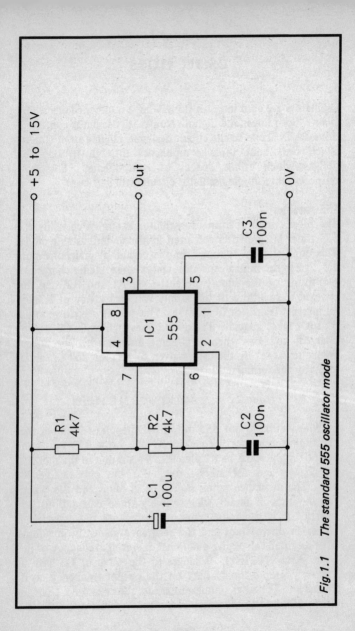

Fig. 1.1 The standard 555 oscillator mode

increasing it to 1μ reduces it to about 100Hz. A bit of mental arithmetic is usually all that is needed to select the values for other output frequencies.

For operation at low frequencies C2 will have to be a good quality electrolytic or (preferably) a tantalum bead capacitor. When using a polarised capacitor the positive terminal connects to pins 6 and 2 of IC1. There is no definite limit on the lowest output frequency that a 555 astable can achieve. Frequencies as low as 0.1Hz can be readily achieved, but at lower frequencies reliability becomes increasingly problematic. High values for C1 become necessary, and leakage through this component then tends to produce unpredictable results, possibly even preventing oscillation. At the high frequency end of the 555's range at least 500kHz can be achieved. Some low power versions can achieve higher frequencies (2.1MHz for the TLC555CP for instance).

For reliable operation the combined resistance of R1 and R2 should be no more than about 10M. The minimum acceptable resistance for R1 depends on the supply voltage used, and is obtained by multiplying the supply potential by five (e.g. 45 ohms with a 9 volt supply). In practice the value of R1 must often be much higher than this minimum value in order to keep the current consumption of the circuit down to an acceptable level. Under low loading the output voltage swing is virtually equal to the supply voltage. The output can source or sink up to 200 milliamps, but it will provide a much reduced output voltage swing when heavily loaded.

The current consumption is about 8 milliamps plus the currents that flow in the timing network and at the output of the 555. Low power versions of the 555 (TLC555CP, L555CP, etc.) have much lower current consumptions of only about 50 to 250 microamps, plus the timing and output currents. However, many of these low power devices have lower output current capabilities which makes them unsuitable for some applications. Note that the standard 555 tends to "crowbar" the supply once per output cycle, which can place a negative voltage spike onto the supply lines. It is therefore advisable to include a supply decoupling capacitor of at least 100μ in value (C1). None of the low power 555s seem to

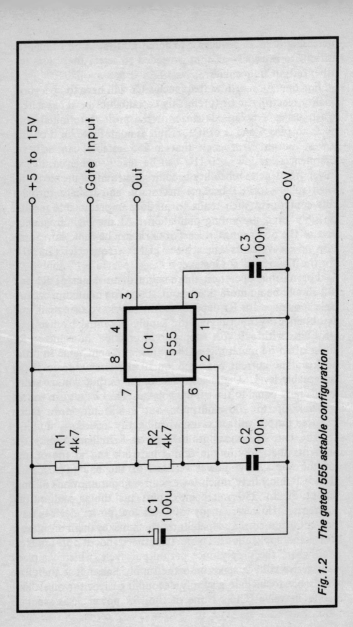

Fig. 1.2   The gated 555 astable configuration

4

suffer from this problem, and with these the supply decoupling can be less stringent.

A 555 astable can be operated as a gated oscillator by applying the gate signal to pin 4 (which is normally tied to the positive supply rail). Figure 1.2 shows the gated 555 astable configuration. A high gate signal produces oscillation — a low input level switches off the oscillator. Note that in this case a low input level means a voltage of less than 0.5 volts.

Pin 5 of a 555 connects to the potential divider circuit which sets the two-thirds of the supply potential threshold level (at which C2 is switched from charging to discharging). Normally this terminal is just left unconnected, or is decoupled by a capacitor to prevent stray pickup. However, a control voltage can be applied to pin 5, effectively converting the circuit to a form of voltage controlled oscillator (v.c.o.). Taking pin 5 above two-thirds of the supply voltage produces a reduction in the output frequency — taking pin 5 below two-thirds of the supply potential gives an increase in output frequency. Figure 1.3 shows the 555 v.c.o. configuration.

There is a slight problem with the standard 555 astable configuration in that it can not produce a squarewave output. The charge time must always be longer than the discharge time, which means that the high output period must always be longer than the low output time. This is due to the fact that the timing capacitor charges up through both timing resistors, but only discharges through one of them. There is a simple solution to this problem, which is to add a couple of steering diodes, as shown in Figure 1.4. The charge path for C2 is via R2 and D2, while the discharge path is via R1 and D1. R1 therefore sets the period for which the output is low, while R2 sets the period for which the output is high. When calculating the output frequency the total timing resistance is therefore simply the sum of R1 and R2 (not R2 plus twice R1).

The specified values give an output frequency of about 1kHz, as in the original design (Fig.1.1). However, in this case R1 has about double the value of R2, giving a mark-space ratio of about 1 to 2 (i.e. the output is high for about half the

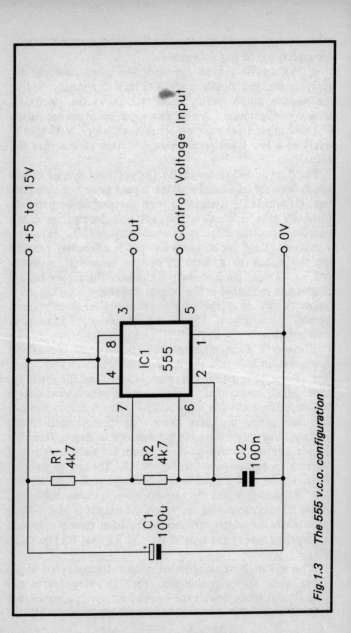

Fig. 1.3 The 555 v.c.o. configuration

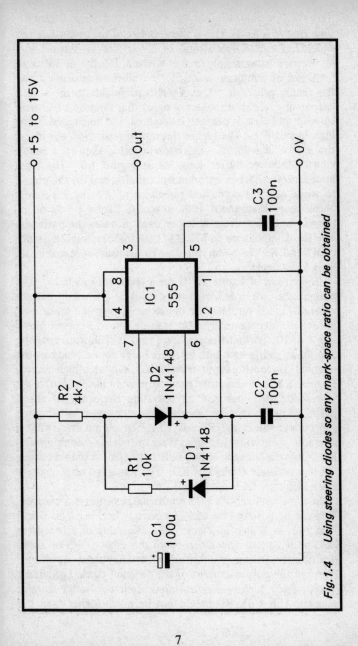

Fig.1.4   Using steering diodes so any mark-space ratio can be obtained

7

time that it is low). This is the opposite of the original design, which has a mark-space ratio of about 2 to 1. For a 1 to 1 mark-space ratio simply make R1 and R2 the same value.

A sort of non-linear triangular waveform is available across the timing capacitor. This signal is preferable to the normal output in applications where a signal that varies in a relatively smooth and steady manner is required, but this signal is at a high impedance. The higher the timing resistance, the higher the source impedance. This signal can be taken via a simple emitter follower buffer stage, as in Figure 1.5. The input impedance to TR1 is by no means infinite, and for this circuit to work well the combined resistance of R2 and R3 should be no more than about 100k or so. In Figure 1.6 an operational amplifier voltage follower stage provides the buffering. The input impedance to IC1 is so high that the total resistance of R2 and R3 can be anything up to the usual 10M maximum for a 555 astable.

The circuit of Figure 1.7 is for a sawtooth oscillator. The timing capacitor is fed with the output of a constant current generator based on TR1. It therefore charges at a linear rate, rather than exponentially. No resistor is used between pins 6 and 7 of IC2 so that the discharge time is as short as possible. The linear charge rate plus brief discharge period produces the required sawtooth output waveform. It is at a high impedance, and IC1 is therefore used to provide output buffering. The specified values give an operating frequency of about 1kHz. Other output frequencies can be obtained by using the appropriate values for R3 and C1. The output frequency is inversely proportional to the values of these two components. R3 should be between about 68R and 680k. A pulsed output signal is available at pin 3 of IC2. This signal is a brief negative pulse each time C1 is discharged.

In some applications a longer discharge period is preferable. This can be achieved by adding a resistor between pins 6 and 7 of IC2, as shown in Figure 1.8. The value of this resistor (R4) must be low in comparison to the value of R3 or it will significantly reduce the linearity of the output waveform. Provided the output current of the constant current generator is kept fairly high, a simple emitter follower buffer stage is adequate (Fig.1.9). R3 should not be much higher than the

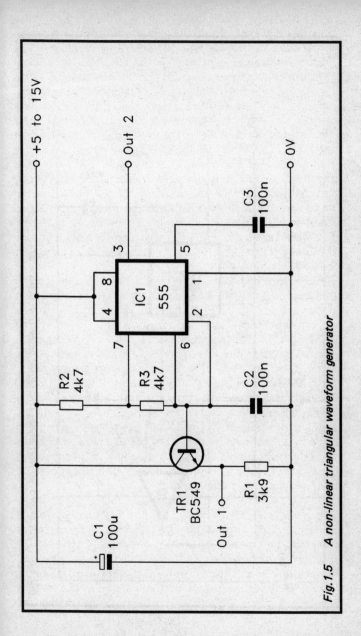

Fig. 1.5 A non-linear triangular waveform generator

9

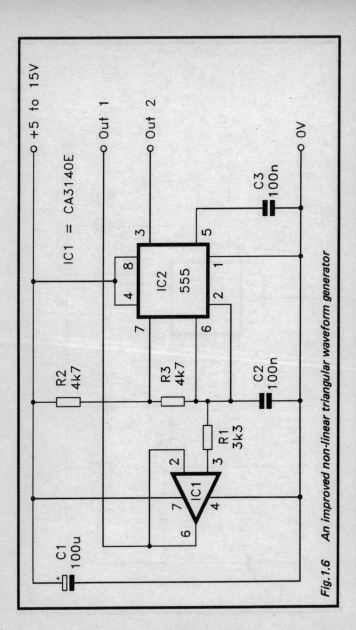

+5 to 15V

Out 1

Out 2

0V

IC1 = CA3140E

IC2 555

3

8

4

7

5

1

2

6

R2 4k7

R3 4k7

C2 100n

C3 100n

R1 3k3

IC1

2

3

7

6

4

C1 100u

Fig.1.6   An improved non-linear triangular waveform generator

10

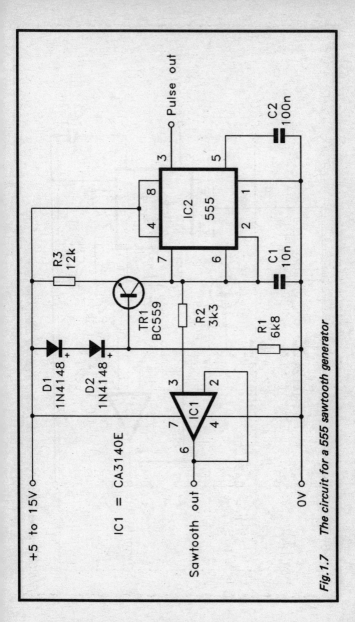

Fig. 1.7 The circuit for a 555 sawtooth generator

11

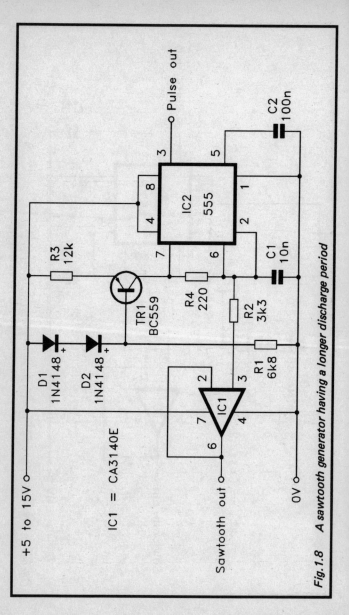

Fig.1.8   A sawtooth generator having a longer discharge period

12

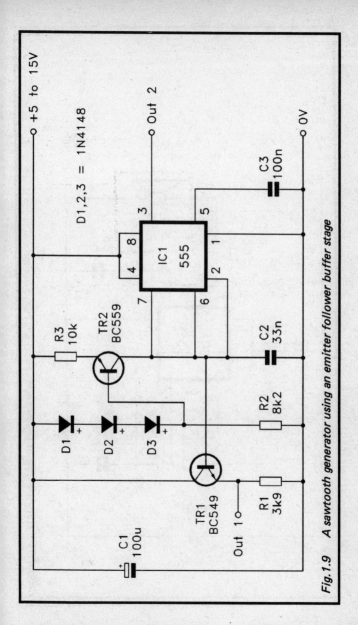

Fig. 1.9   A sawtooth generator using an emitter follower buffer stage

13

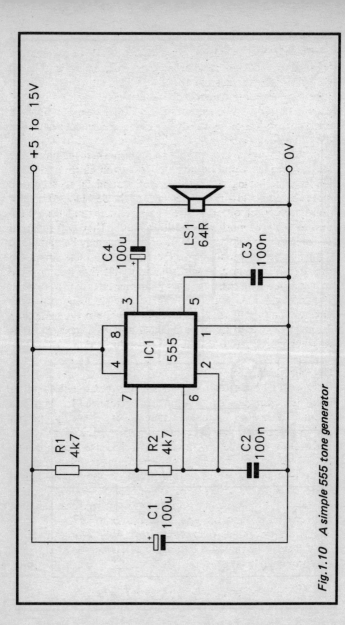

Fig.1.10 A simple 555 tone generator

14

specified value.

The 555 has an output stage which can drive a miniature high impedance loudspeaker at good volume. Figure 1.10 shows the circuit diagram for a tone generator of this type. It is not advisable to drive the loudspeaker direct from the output of IC1 as this can result in a rather high current consumption and poor reliability. Results are much better if a d.c. blocking capacitor (C4) is included. It is also not advisable to use a low impedance loudspeaker, for much the same reasons. Good results should be obtained using any loudspeaker having an impedance of around 50 to 80 ohms. Note that some low power versions of the 555 have decidedly non-symmetrical output drive characteristics, and that these devices will not work well in this circuit. They will function to some extent, but the volume of the tone may be quite low.

A number of variations on the basic 555 astable circuit are provided here, and it is worth pointing out that it is possible to use several of these variations in one circuit if necessary. For instance, it is quite in order to gate the tone generator circuit via a gate signal applied to pin 4, while at the same time frequency modulating it via a signal applied to pin 5. It is this versatility that makes the 555 so useful.

Op Amp Oscillators

What could be regarded as the standard operational amplifier oscillator configuration is shown in Figure 1.11. This is a form of relaxation oscillator where C2 is repeatedly charged and discharged via R4. The operating frequency of the circuit is therefore controlled by the values of these two components. R4 should be at least a few hundred ohms in value, and can be up to many megohms in value if a f.e.t. input stage operational amplifier is used (CA3140E, LF351N, TL081CP, etc.). C2 can be a polarised type, and the positive terminal then connects to R3 and R4. As is the case with all C − R oscillators, the operating frequency is inversely proportional to the values of the timing components. The operating frequency is approximately equal to:

$$\text{Frequency} = 0.8/(R4 \times C2) \text{ hertz}$$

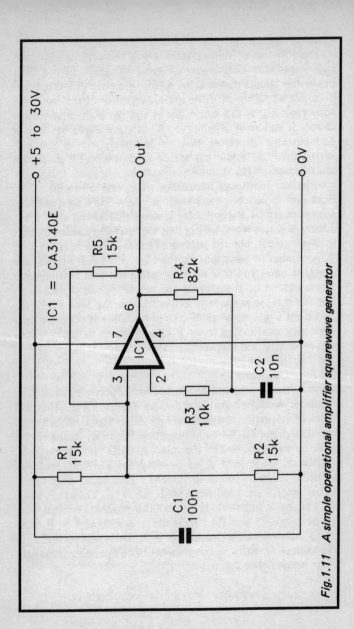

Fig. 1.11 A simple operational amplifier squarewave generator

+5 to 30V

Out

0V

IC1 = CA3140E

R5 15k

R4 82k

R1 15k

R3 10k

R2 15k

C1 100n

C2 10n

7

3

6

IC1

2

4

This results in an operating frequency of just under 1kHz with the specified values. Protection resistor R3 is only needed for operational amplifiers which have MOS input stages. For other types (including bifet operational amplifiers) it can be replaced with a shorting link. The output waveform is a squarewave having a reasonably accurate 1 to 1 mark-space ratio. Although in theory the mark-space ratio is exactly 1 to 1, in reality the operational amplifier will almost certainly have slightly non-symmetrical output characteristics which will slightly distort the mark-space ratio.

The signal across C2 is a sort of non-linear triangular waveform. This can be used as the main output signal if desired, but as it is at a high impedance a buffer stage must be used. This is just a matter of adding an operational amplifier voltage follower stage, just the same as in the 555 circuit of Figure 1.6 which was described previously. However, the squarewave/triangular waveform generator described later in this chapter might be a better choice where triangular type waveform is required.

Where dual supplies are available the slightly simplified configuration of Figure 1.12 can be used. For mark-space ratios of other than 1 to 1, steering diodes can be added to the timing network. Figure 1.13 shows the circuit diagram for an oscillator which includes steering diodes (Figure 1.14 shows the dual supply version). R4 controls the period for which the output is low — R6 controls the high output duration. With two resistors in the timing network the formula for calculating the operating frequency becomes slightly different to the one for the standard version of the oscillator. The modified formula for the circuit of Figure 1.13 is:

$$\text{Frequency} = 1.6/(R4 + R6) \, C2 \text{ hertz}$$

The specified timing component values give an operating frequency of about 1kHz, and a mark-space ratio of 1 to 15. The mark-space ratio is controlled by the ratio of R6 to R4.

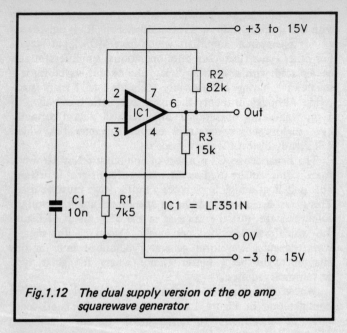

*Fig.1.12   The dual supply version of the op amp
squarewave generator*

Sinewave Generators

For a sinewave output signal a Wien oscillator is a popular
choice.   This type of oscillator can provide a very high
quality sinewave output signal, and distortion levels of under
0.1% are readily achieved.   However, for such good quality
results the feedback level must be very accurately stabilised.
In the circuit of Figure 1.15 the feedback is stabilised by an
RA53 (or R53) self heating thermistor.   This is a relatively
expensive component, but it gives excellent results and permits
a very simple circuit to be used.   The output level is approximately 2 volts peak to peak.

The operating frequency is governed by the values of R3,
R5, C3, and C4.   R3 and R5 should have the same value, as
should C3 and C4.   The specified values give an operating
frequency of approximately 1kHz, but the values of the timing
components can be altered to give any operating frequency
from the sub-audio range to a frequency of up to about 1MHz.
If a variable frequency sinewave oscillator is required, R3 and

18

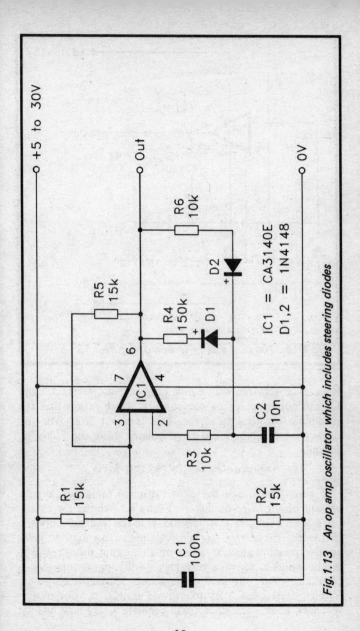

Fig.1.13 An op amp oscillator which includes steering diodes

+5 to 30V

Out

0V

R6 10k

D2

IC1 = CA3140E
D1,2 = 1N4148

R5 15k

R4 150k

D1

7   6

IC1

3   4

2

C2 10n

R3 10k

R1 15k

R2 15k

C1 100n

19

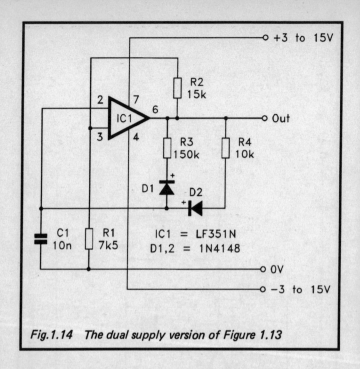

Fig.1.14 The dual supply version of Figure 1.13

R5 can be replaced with a dual gang potentiometer. C3 and C4 can not be polarised components, which means that the maximum practical value for these is about $2\mu2$. The frequency of oscillation can be calculated using the following formula:

$$\text{Frequency} = 1/6.283\,C\,R \text{ hertz}$$

Figure 1.16 shows the circuit diagram for a dual supply version of the Wien oscillator. Figure 1.17 shows the circuit for a Wien oscillator that uses diodes in the feedback network to prevent excessively strong oscillation. This method gives relatively high distortion levels on the output though, and it is not suitable where a very high quality sinewave signal is required. The output level is about 500 millivolts r.m.s.

Figure 1.18 has VR1 to provide manual control of the feedback level. The circuit will generate a very high quality

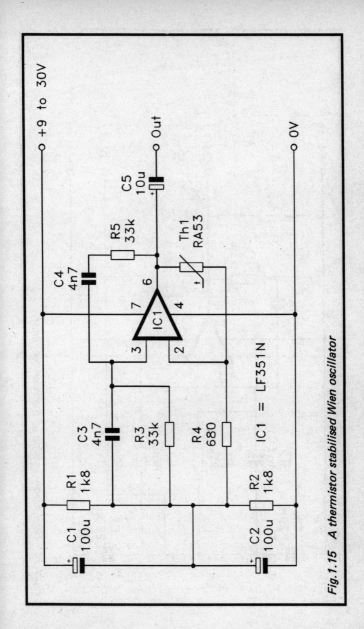

Fig. 1.15 A thermistor stabilised Wien oscillator

21

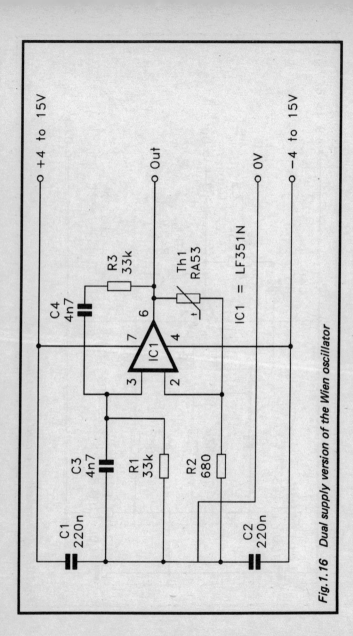

Fig.1.16 Dual supply version of the Wien oscillator

22

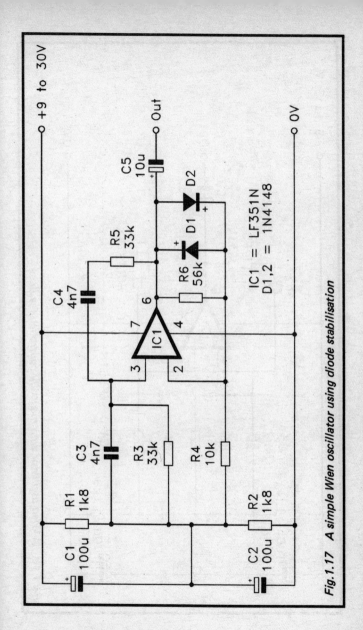

Fig.1.17 A simple Wien oscillator using diode stabilisation

IC1 = LF351N
D1,2 = 1N4148

23

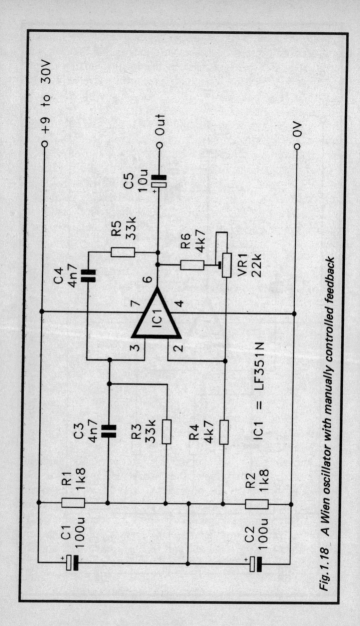

Fig. 1.18 A Wien oscillator with manually controlled feedback

sinewave signal provided VR1 is given a setting which keeps the output signal well below the clipping level. VR1 should be a multi-turn preset resistor. Note that as this circuit has no feedback stabilisation, changes in the loading on the output can have a significant effect on the output level and signal quality. These loading affects can be largely eliminated by adding a buffer stage at the output of the circuit. The output level is dependent on the setting of VR1, and can be anything from a few hundred millivolts peak to peak to several volts peak to peak.

The circuit of Figure 1.19 is for a Wien oscillator based on an LM380N audio power amplifier. This provides sufficient output to drive an 8 ohm impedance loudspeaker at about 1 to 2 watts r.m.s. VR1 controls the feedback level, and is set to give the required volume level. Low volume levels give a higher quality sinewave output.

A phase shift oscillator is another form of sinewave generator, and it is usually based on a bipolar transistor used in the common emitter mode (Fig.1.20). This type of circuit does not provide a particularly high quality output signal, but it is adequate for many applications. Phase shift oscillators have a reputation for poor reliability, but this circuit will work well provided a high gain transistor is used for TR1, and the value of R1 and R2 is not varied much from the specified figure of 10k. Accordingly, changes in frequency must be accomplished by using a different value for C1 to C3, and not by altering the value of R1 and R2. The specified value of 6n8 provides oscillation at approximately 1kHz. Operation over the full audio range is possible, but the circuit is unlikely to work well much outside this range.

Although phase shift oscillators are normally based on common emitter amplifiers, they work just as well (or even better) if based on an operational amplifier. The circuit diagram for a phase shift oscillator based on an operational amplifier is shown in Figure 1.21. The input and output of a common emitter amplifier are 180 degrees out-of-phase, and IC1 is therefore operated in the inverting mode. VR1 controls the closed loop voltage gain of IC1. It is set to give a good compromise between strong and reliable oscillation on the one hand, and purity of the output signal on the other.

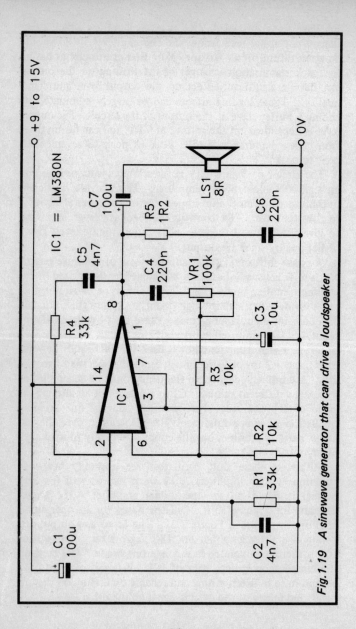

Fig. 1.19 A sinewave generator that can drive a loudspeaker

26

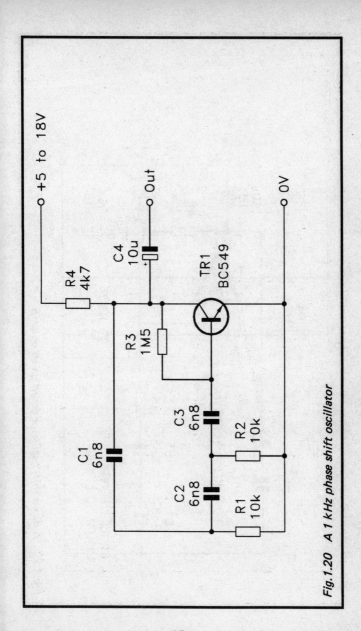

Fig. 1.20 A 1 kHz phase shift oscillator

27

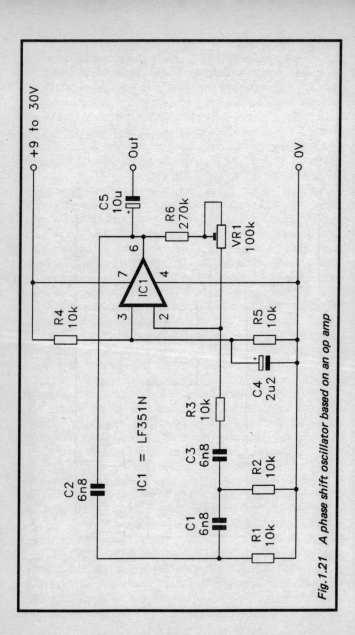

Fig.1.21 A phase shift oscillator based on an op amp

28

Function Generators

The circuit of Figure 1.22 is for a useful oscillator which provides square and triangular output signals. The triangular signal is a high quality type having good linearity, although the quality of both signals falls away somewhat at high operating frequencies. C2 and R4 are the timing components, and the specified values provide oscillation at approximately 1kHz. R4 should have a value of about 1k or more, and C2 should not be a polarised type. Figure 1.23 shows the circuit diagram for the dual supply version of this circuit.

Adding a diode across the timing resistor converts the circuit to one which provides pulse and sawtooth output signals (Fig.1.24). The sawtooth waveform is of the type which ramps in a positive direction, and then drops back negatively almost instantly. The pulse signal is a series of brief positive pulses. Connecting D1 with the opposite polarity gives a negative ramp signal and brief negative output pulses. Note that adding D1 effectively halves the timing resistance, since R4 is effectively short circuited during one set of half cycles. The specified values therefore give operation at about 2kHz (use a 68k resistor for R4 to give an output frequency of approximately 1kHz). A resistor in series with D1 will lengthen the output pulses, and increase the recovery period between the ramp sections of the sawtooth output.

Figure 1.25 shows the circuit diagram for a function generator based on the 8038 integrated circuit. Figure 1.26 shows an alternative version which has an emitter follower output buffer stage in place of the operational amplifier voltage follower. The operational amplifier stage gives better isolation between IC1 and the load, but the emitter follower is faster (which gives a better squarewave output signal). There are several versions of the 8038, as indicated by various suffix letters. They differ in the guaranteed level of performance provided. The only version sold by most component retailers is the 8038CC, which offers a sinewave distortion level of under 1% for frequencies of less than 10kHz.

The 8038 offers three output waveforms, which are square, triangular, and sinewave. In these circuits a switch is used to select the desired output waveform, but all three outputs of IC1 can be used simultaneously if a separate buffer is provided

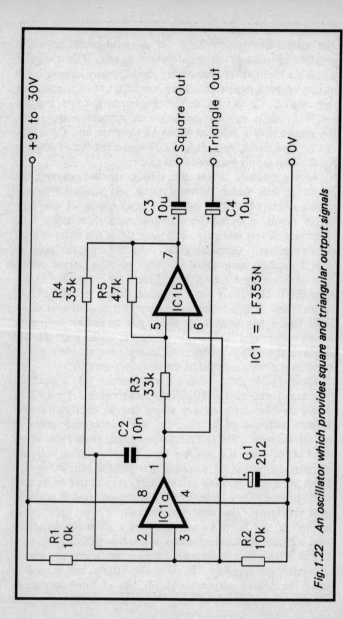

Fig.1.22 An oscillator which provides square and triangular output signals

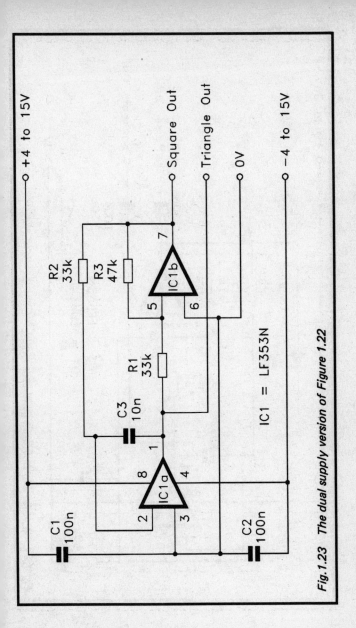

Fig. 1.23 The dual supply version of Figure 1.22

31

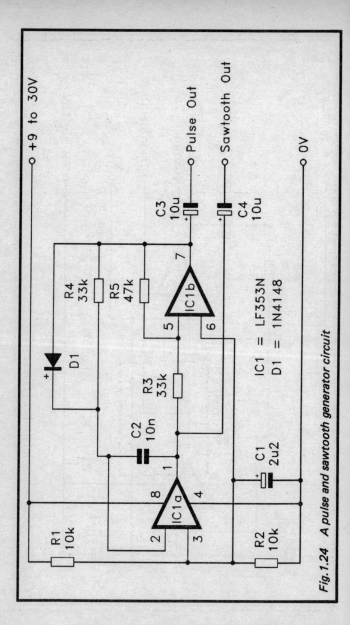

Fig. 1.24 A pulse and sawtooth generator circuit

32

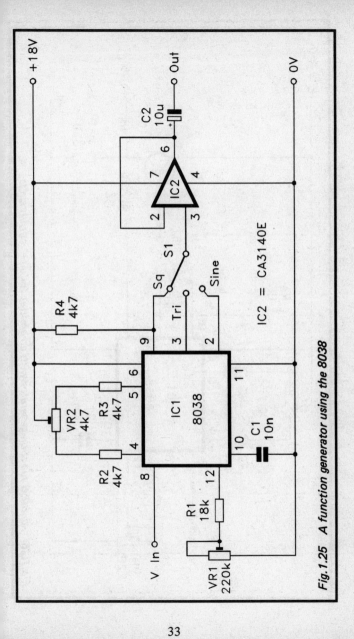

Fig.1.25 A function generator using the 8038

33

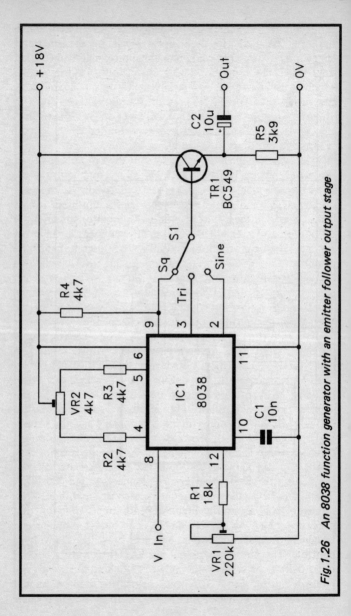

Fig. 1.26 An 8038 function generator with an emitter follower output stage

34

for each one. The three output signals are at different amplitudes. The peak to peak signal levels of the sinewave, triangular, and squarewave signals are approximately 0.22, 0.3, 0.99 times the supply voltage (respectively). Although the supply voltage is given as 18 volts in Figures 1.25 and 1.26, the circuit will work quite well on supply voltages down to 10 volts. However, lower supply voltages do give some reduction in performance. The current consumption of the circuit is about 16 milliamps from an 18 volt supply.

VR2 controls the mark-space ratio of the output signal, and this would normally be set for a ratio of 1 to 1 with the aid of an oscilloscope. VR1 controls the purity of the sinewave output signal, and would ideally be set for optimum results using distortion measuring equipment to monitor the sinewave output signal. In the absence of such equipment it can be set for the best waveform displayed on an oscilloscope, or for the purest sounding signal (i.e. the one with the lowest high frequency content). VR1 and R1 can simply be omitted if something less than optimum performance is acceptable.

The 8038 is a form of voltage controlled oscillator (v.c.o.). With the specified values the circuit oscillates at approximately 200Hz with the control input at the full positive supply potential of 18 volts. Using a lower input voltage results in a higher output frequency. Reducing the control voltage by about 1.5 volts boosts the output frequency to 2kHz, while reducing it by 6 volts gives an output frequency of around 10kHz. Lower control voltages result in oscillation ceasing.

C1 is the only discrete timing component, and the operating frequency range of the circuit can be altered by using a different value for this component. Any value of more than about 33p can be used, and polarised capacitors are suitable. With the latter the positive terminal connects to pin 10 of IC1. The circuit will operate at frequencies of up to about 1MHz.

Figure 1.27 shows the circuit diagram for a simple function generator based on the NE566N. This provides square and triangular output waveforms, and has provision for voltage control. The output frequency is about 1kHz with a control potential of 10 volts, reducing to only about 5Hz with the control voltage about 0.1 volts below the positive supply potential. Taking the control input right up to the full positive

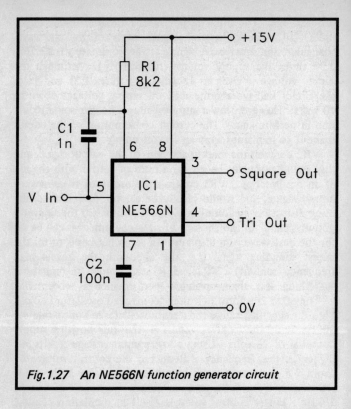

Fig.1.27   An NE566N function generator circuit

supply voltage causes oscillation to cease, as does taking it
below about half the supply voltage.   Although a 15 volt
supply is specified in Figure 1.27, the circuit will function
over a supply voltage range of 10 to 24 volts at a current
consumption of approximately 7 milliamps.

   R1 and C2 are the timing components, and the values of
these can be altered to give different operating frequency
ranges.   R1 should be between 2k and 20k, while C2 can
have any value that keeps the output frequency within the
1MHz maximum rating of the NE566N.   C2 can be a polarised type, and the positive terminal is then the one which
connects to IC1 pin 7.

V.C.O.s

Note that in addition to the v.c.o. circuits described in this section, there are v.c.o.s in other sections of this chapter (including those in the previous section on function generators). The circuits described in this section have what are, in general, better control characteristics for many v.c.o. applications.

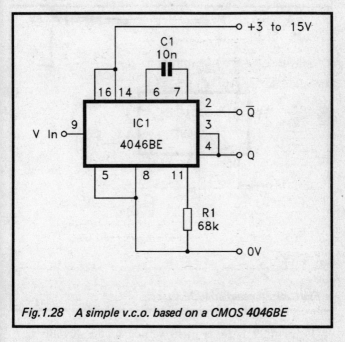

Fig.1.28 A simple v.c.o. based on a CMOS 4046BE

The circuit of Figure 1.28 is for a simple v.c.o. based on a CMOS 4046BE micro-power phase locked loop. In this case it is basically just the v.c.o. section that is used, although one of the phase comparators is used as a simple inverter to provide the anti-phase not-Q output. The outputs are good quality squarewaves. C1 and R1 are the timing components, and with the specified values the output frequency is about 250Hz per volt. The linearity is very good (typically better than 1%), but bear in mind that about 0.6 volts is needed at the control input before oscillation will occur. Also bear in mind that the control voltage must not exceed the positive supply potential. A frequency span of over 1000 to 1 can be accommodated via the control input, and output frequencies of up to 500kHz can be achieved. R1 can have any value between 10k and 10M, while C1 can be any non-polarised capacitor having a value of more than 50p.

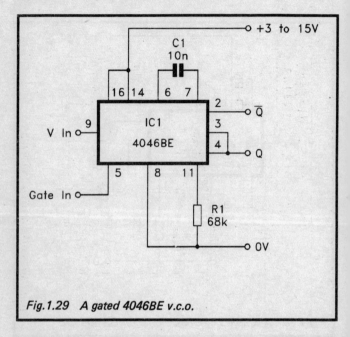

Fig.1.29   A gated 4046BE v.c.o.

Figure 1.29 is for a gated version of the 4046BE v.c.o. This makes use of the inhibit input at pin 5 of IC1. Taking this high cuts off the v.c.o. — taking it low permits normal operation.

The circuit of Figure 1.30 is for a v.c.o. based on one section of an LM13700N (or LM13600N) transconductance amplifier. The output waveform is a sort of kinked triangular waveform. With the specified value for C2 the circuit provides an output frequency of 1kHz with an input potential of 10 volts. The linearity is quite good, but like the 4046BE v.c.o.

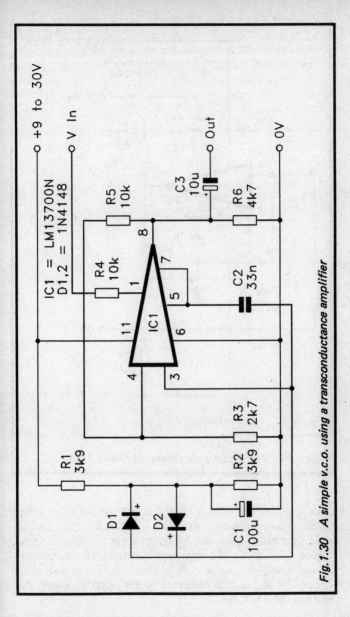

Fig. 1.30 A simple v.c.o. using a transconductance amplifier

39

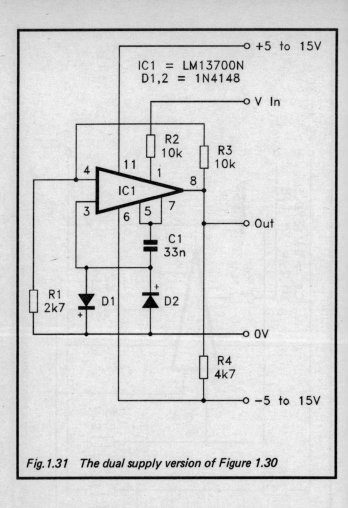

Fig.1.31 The dual supply version of Figure 1.30

circuit, about 0.6 volts is needed at the control input before oscillation commences. Also like the 4046BE v.c.o., a very wide frequency span can be covered via the control input. Figure 1.31 shows the dual supply version of the transconductance amplifier v.c.o. Note that with this version of the circuit "V in" is with reference to the negative supply rail, and not the 0 volt rail.

40

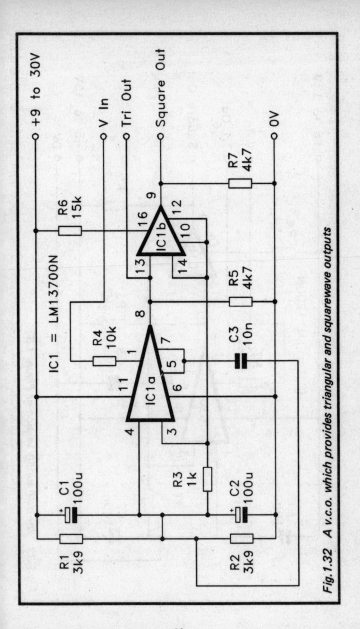

Fig.1.32 A v.c.o. which provides triangular and squarewave outputs

41

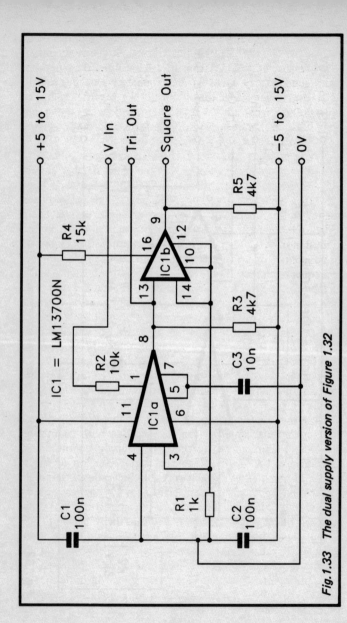

Fig. 1.33   The dual supply version of Figure 1.32

42

Figure 1.32 is for a v.c.o. that utilizes both sections of an LM13700N (or LM13600N) dual transconductance amplifier. This is a sort of v.c.o. version of a basic function generator, giving good quality triangular and squarewave output signals. C3 is the timing capacitor, and with the specified value an input voltage range of 0.6 to 12 volts will sweep the circuit from sub-audio frequencies into the ultrasonic range. Figure 1.33 shows the dual supply version of this v.c.o.

A very useful v.c.o. circuit is shown in Figure 1.34. This is another variation on the basic function generator circuit, and despite its simplicity this circuit provides very good linearity. With the specified value for C1 the output frequency is approximately 1kHz with an input voltage of 10 volts. C1 can have any value of more than about 50p, but it must not be a polarised type. The circuit will operate well at frequencies of up to 20kHz, and with reduced performance at frequencies of up to at least 100kHz. The mark-space ratio of the squarewave signal is controlled by R2 and R3, and quite high ratios can be achieved. However, the mark-space ratio is not equal to the ratio of R2 to R3. The ratio of these resistors must be between 1 to 2 and 2 to 1. Ratios outside these limits try to set mark-space ratios beyond infinity, and the circuit then fails to oscillate. Of course, changes in the mark-space ratio of the squarewave signal are accompanied by corresponding distortions in the timing of the triangular signal.

Note that the single supply version of this v.c.o. requires a dual operational amplifier that can operate with its outputs at voltages almost equal to the 0 volt supply potential (e.g. LM358N or CA3240E). The dual supply version of Figure 1.35 will work using virtually any dual operational amplifier.

Figure 1.36 shows the basic circuit for a v.c.o. based on the LM331N. This provides excellent linearity with an output frequency that is approximately equal to 1kHz per volt. The output signal is a pulsed signal incidentally, and note that its mark-space ratio changes somewhat with variations in the control voltage. R1 and C1 are the timing components. By using different values for C1 a wide range of full scale frequencies can be achieved. C1 can be a polarised capacitor (with the positive terminal connected to IC1 pin 5), but for

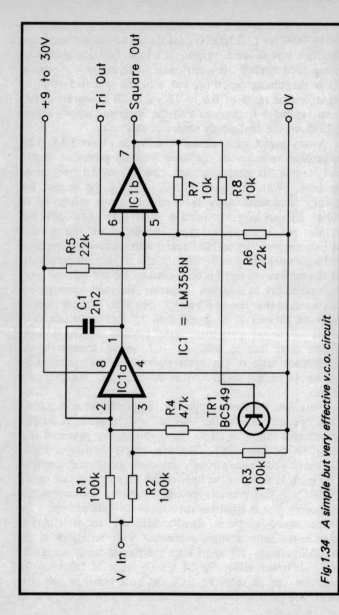

Fig. 1.34 A simple but very effective v.c.o. circuit

44

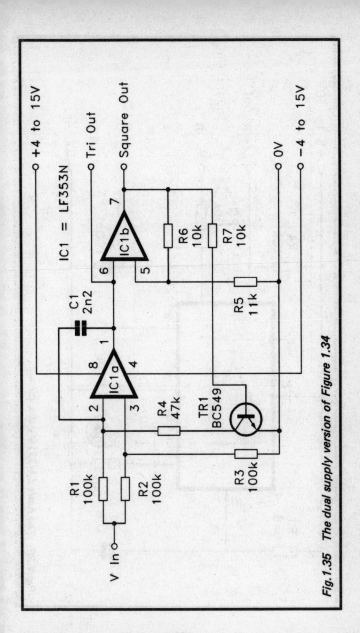

Fig. 1.35 The dual supply version of Figure 1.34

45

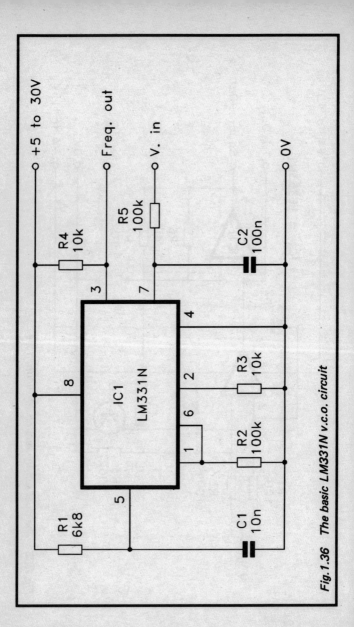

Fig.1.36 The basic LM331N v.c.o. circuit

46

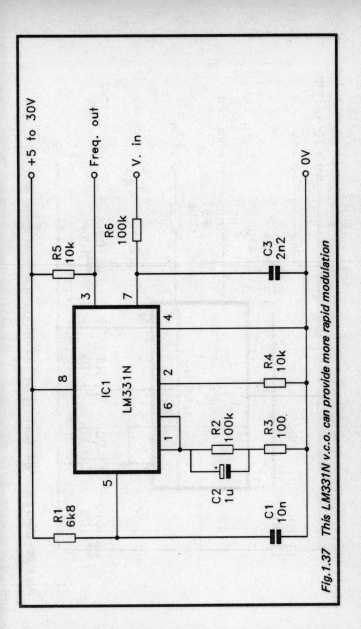

Fig. 1.37 This LM331N v.c.o. can provide more rapid modulation

47

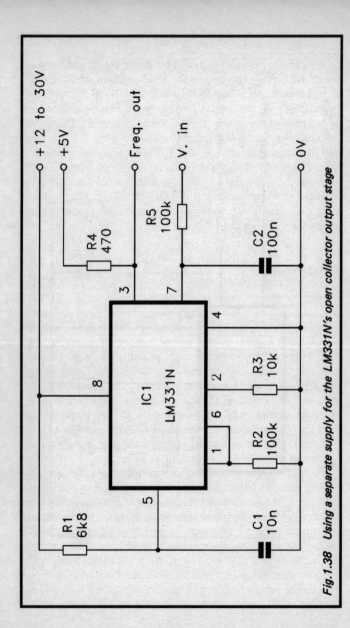

Fig. 1.38 Using a separate supply for the LM331N's open collector output stage

48

optimum results it should be a good quality non-polarised capacitor.

R5 and C2 act as a lowpass filter at the input, and for good results with this basic circuit the time constant of R5 and C2 must be very much higher than that of R1 and C1. If rapid modulations of the output frequency are required, the modified configuration of Figure 1.37 should be used. This avoids any tendency for the oscillator to stall.

The output terminal at pin 3 of IC1 is an open collector type. This makes it possible to run the v.c.o. from a supply potential of between 12 and 30 volts, with a 5 volt logic compatible output signal still being provided. It is just a matter of using the 5 volt logic supply for the output transistor, as shown in Figure 1.38.

CMOS Oscillators

Figure 1.39 shows the circuit diagram for a basic CMOS oscillator. This is shown as using NAND gates from a 4011BE, but these gates are just connected as inverters, and any standard CMOS inverters or gates connected to function as inverters will work properly in this circuit. Note though, that high output current inverters are not recommended for operation in linear circuits, which includes oscillators. Using a high current buffer could result in it drawing an excessive supply current. IC1a and IC1b are the active components in the oscillator circuit, while IC1c provides an anti-phase output (and can be omitted if anti-phase output signals are not required). The output signal is roughly square, but is unlikely to have an accurate 1 to 1 mark-space ratio.

R1 and C1 are the timing components, and the specified values give an approximate output frequency of 1kHz. However, the exact output frequency varies significantly from one device to another, and also varies slightly with changes in the supply voltage. This type of oscillator is not recommended for use where high performance is required. R1 can have any value from about 4k7 to 10M. C1 can have any value of more than about 10p, but it should not be a polarised type. The circuit will operate well at frequencies of up to about 500kHz.

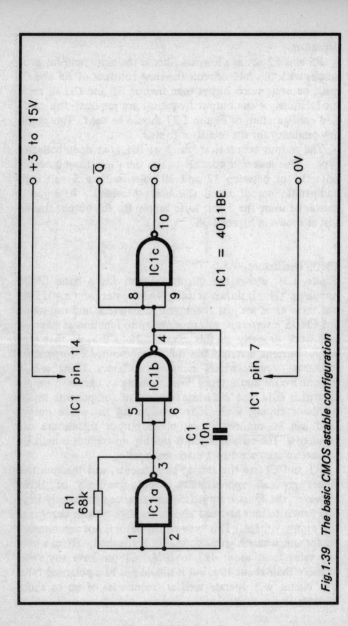

Fig. 1.39 The basic CMOS astable configuration

+3 to 15V

Q̄

Q

0V

IC1 = 4011BE

IC1 pin 14

IC1 pin 7

IC1c
10
8
9

IC1b
4
5
6

IC1a
3
1
2

R1
68k

C1
10n

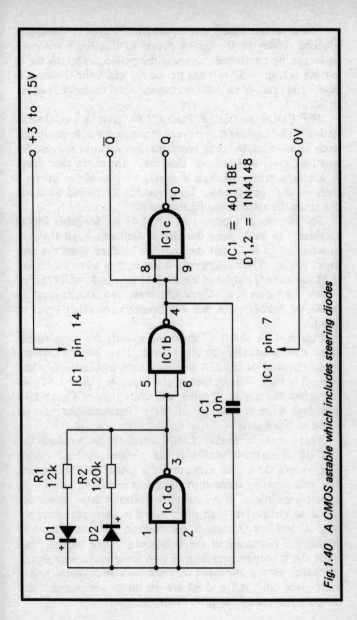

Fig. 1.40 A CMOS astable which includes steering diodes

+3 to 15V

Q̄

Q

0V

10

IC1c

8   9

IC1 = 4011BE
D1,2 = 1N4148

IC1 pin 14

4

IC1b

5   6

C1
10n

IC1 pin 7

R1
12k

R2
120k

D1

D2

3

IC1a

1   2

The modified CMOS astable circuit of Figure 1.40 includes steering diodes in the timing circuit so that the mark-space ratio can be controlled. R1 sets the period for which the Q output is high − R2 sets the period for which the Q output is low. The mark-space ratio is roughly equal to the ratio of R1 to R2.

The CMOS astable of Figure 1.41 gives a crude v.c.o. action. This enables it to be used in simple v.c.o. applications, such as a modulated tone generator, but it is not suitable for anything more sophisticated than this. The modulation range is not very great, although it should be possible to obtain a shift of over one octave. Input resistor R1 should be about ten times the value of timing resistor R2.

The circuits of Figures 1.42 and 1.43 are for gated CMOS astables. In both cases the circuit oscillates when the gate input is taken high, and oscillation is blocked when the gate input is low. The circuits only differ in that when oscillation is blocked the Q output of Figure 1.42 goes high, while that of Figure 1.43 goes low. Obviously these two circuits must be based on NAND gates and not inverters (or other types of gate).

Figures 1.44 and 1.45 show the circuits for complement gated CMOS astables. In other words, these circuits oscillate when the control input is low, and have oscillation blocked when it is high. The output of the circuit in Figure 1.44 goes low when the circuit is gated off, while that of Figure 1.45 goes high when it is in the off state. These circuits must be based on NOR gates.

Where a high quality CMOS oscillator is required the 4047BE monostable/astable is the obvious choice. Figure 1.46 shows the circuit diagram for a gated 4047BE astable. The gate input is taken high to enable oscillation, or low to disable oscillation. If a free-running astable is required, use the same circuit but with pin 5 wired to the positive supply rail. Q and not Q outputs are available, as is an output at double the frequency of the Q outputs. Note though, that while the Q outputs provide a very accurate squarewave signal, the signal on the 2f output may not have an accurate 1 to 1 mark-space ratio. C1 and R1 are the timing components, and the output frequency is given by this formula:

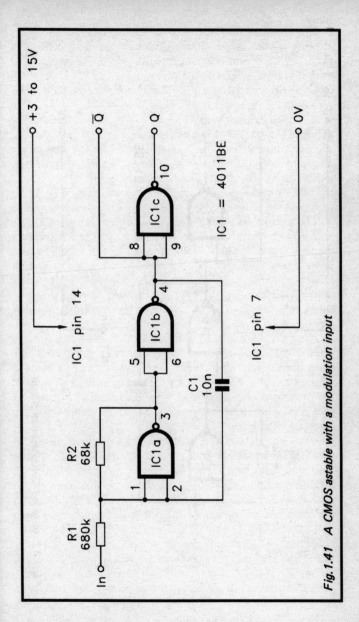

Fig. 1.41 A CMOS astable with a modulation input

53

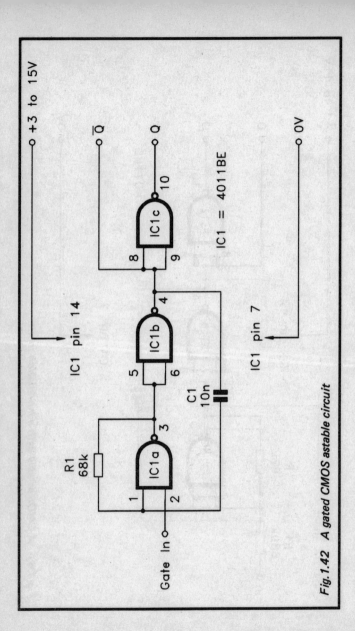

Fig. 1.42 A gated CMOS astable circuit

+3 to 15V

Q̄

Q

IC1c
10
8
9

IC1 = 4011BE

IC1 pin 14

IC1b
4
5
6

0V

IC1 pin 7

IC1a
3
1
2

R1
68k

C1
10n

Gate In

54

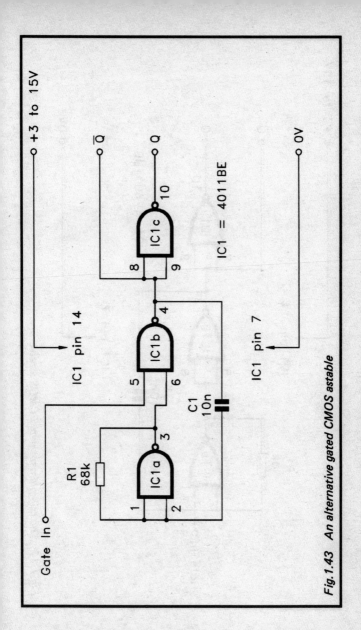

Fig. 1.43 An alternative gated CMOS astable

55

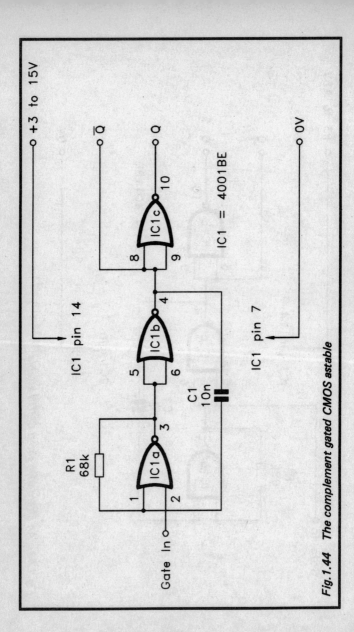

+3 to 15V

IC1 pin 14

$\overline{Q}$

Q

IC1c
8
9
10

IC1b
5
6
4

IC1a
1
2
3

R1
68k

C1
10n

IC1 pin 7

0V

IC1 = 4001BE

Gate In

Fig. 1.44   The complement gated CMOS astable

56

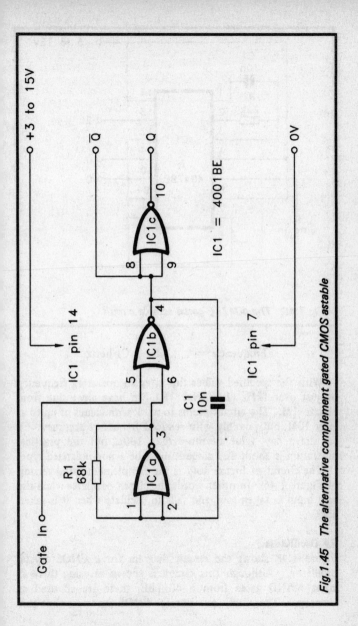

Fig. 1.45 The alternative complement gated CMOS astable

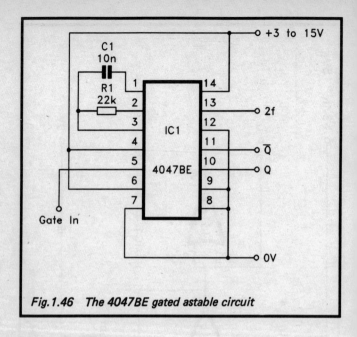

Fig.1.46   The 4047BE gated astable circuit

$$\text{Frequency} = 1/4.4 \; R1 \times C1 \; \text{hertz}$$

With the specified values this gives an operating frequency of just over 1kHz (1.033Hz). R1 can have any value from 10k to 1M. The circuit seems to work with values of up to at least 10M, but possibly with reduced frequency accuracy. C1 can have any value of more than 100p, but the practical maximum is about 2µ2 since it must be a non-polarised type.

The circuit of Figure 1.47 is the complement gated version of Figure 1.46. In other words the circuit oscillates when the gate input is taken low, and fails to oscillate when it is taken high.

RF Oscillators

Figure 1.48 shows the circuit diagram for a CMOS crystal oscillator. Although this circuit is shown as using three 2-input NAND gates from a 4011BE, these are all used as inverters. Therefore, any normal CMOS inverters (but not

58

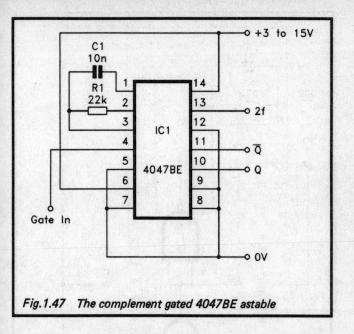

high output current types) or gates connected to give an
inverter action should work properly in this circuit. IC1a
is used in the actual oscillator, while IC1b acts as an amplifier
which provides buffering and gives a better output waveform.
IC1c provides the anti-phase not Q output, and this inverter
should obviously be omitted if anti-phase outputs are not
required.

The circuit will operate over quite a wide frequency range
of at least 0.5MHz to 5MHz. With low frequency crystals
it will probably be advantageous to make C1 and C2 a little
higher in value. Operation down to 200kHz should then be
possible. For operation at frequencies of a few megahertz it
is advisable to make C1 and C2 significantly lower in value.
With C1 and C2 at around 22p in value the circuit should
operate quite well at frequencies of around 6 to 10MHz.
Operation at frequencies much higher than this is not generally
possible as higher frequency crystals are almost invariably
overtone types. These will only work properly in circuits

59

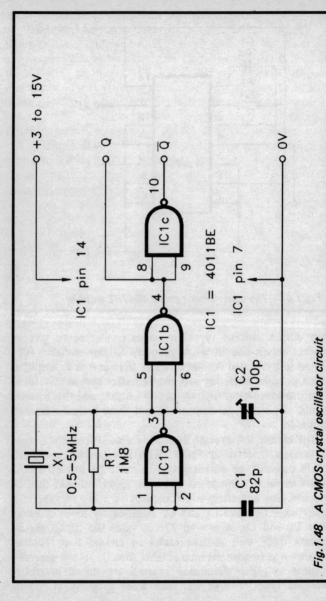

Fig.1.48 A CMOS crystal oscillator circuit

designed specifically for operation with overtone crystals.

C2 can be adjusted to trim the output frequency to precisely the required figure. If this facility is not required then C2 can be replaced with a fixed capacitor having a slightly lower value than C1. The circuit is designed for operation with parallel resonant crystals. It will work with series resonant types, but there will be an error of around 2kHz in the output frequency.

The circuit of Figure 1.49 is for a simple crystal oscillator and buffer amplifier based on two bipolar transistors. The notes about C1, C2, and the crystal in the circuit of Figure 1.48 apply also to the same components in this circuit.

As pointed out previously, crystals having operating frequencies of much more than about 10MHz are usually of the overtone variety. This basically means that they have an operating frequency that is a fraction of their marked frequency (often a third, fifth, seventh, or ninth of the marked frequency). When used in an ordinary crystal oscillator an overtone crystal oscillates at its fundamental frequency, not on the overtone frequency. In order to produce oscillation on the overtone a circuit specifically designed for this type of crystal is required (and the crystal must be a proper overtone type).

In practice this means using an oscillator which includes an L − C tuned circuit operating at the overtone frequency. Figure 1.50 shows the circuit diagram for a simple crystal overtone oscillator. L1 and C2 are the L − C tuned circuit. Either L1 or C2 would normally be a variable component so that the resonant frequency of the tuned circuit could be trimmed to precisely the correct figure. Adjustment of the tuned circuit usually permits the output frequency to be pulled a few kilohertz either side of the crystal frequency. The circuit should operate at frequencies of up to 100MHz or so.

The circuit of Figure 1.51 is for an L − C oscillator which requires a single untapped winding on the coil (L1). The tuned circuit is comprised of L1 and C2, but note that C2 is shunted by the input capacitance of TR1, and the series capacitance of C3 and C4. This gives a minimum tuning capacitance of about 40p or so, which slightly narrows the tuning range available by varying the value of C2. The

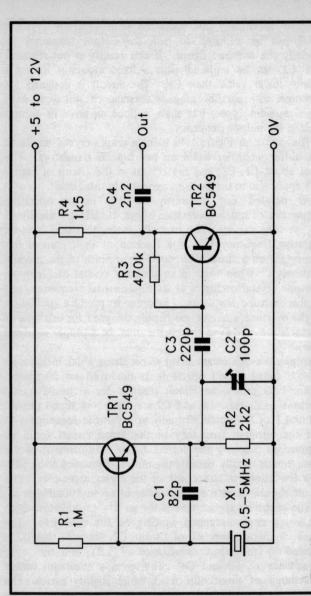

Fig. 1.49 A crystal oscillator and amplifier using bipolar transistors

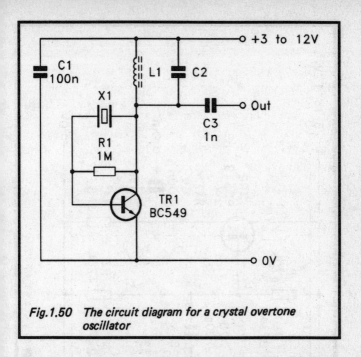

Fig.1.50 The circuit diagram for a crystal overtone oscillator

maximum acceptable value for C2 is about 400p. With suitable L − C values the circuit will operate at any frequency from around 200kHz to 30MHz or so.

The L − C oscillator of Figure 1.52 is very simple, but it requires an r.f. transformer and not a single winding. The tuned circuit is formed by C3 and the large winding of r.f. transformer T1. In practice T1 would be something like a Toko short wave oscillator coil or an i.f. transformer. Note that the phasing of the small coupling winding on T1 must be correct or the circuit will not oscillate. With a suitable r.f. transformer and tuning capacitance the circuit will operate at any frequency from a few tens of kilohertz to 50MHz or more.

Etcetera

The circuit of Figure 1.53 is for a simple but useful relaxation oscillator based on an LS TTL inverting trigger/buffer. The output signal is (more or less) a squarewave signal, and the

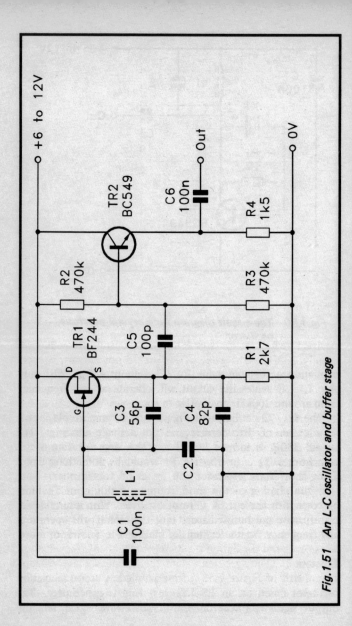

Fig. 1.51 An L-C oscillator and buffer stage

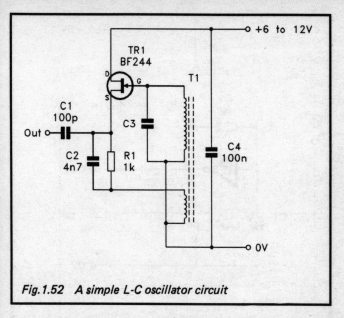

Fig.1.52 A simple L-C oscillator circuit

specified values for C1 and R1 give an output frequency of
roughly 200Hz. The value of R1 should not be varied much
from the specified value of 1k or the circuit will fail to operate. C1 can have any value from a few picofarads upwards,
and the circuit will operate at frequencies of up to a few
megahertz. The circuit will work using a standard 7414, but
R1 will then need to be made much lower in value (a value of
around 330R should be suitable). Note that the circuit will
only work using trigger/buffer devices, and will fail to operate
if simple inverters are used.

Figure 1.54 shows a modification of this circuit which
converts the simple L – C relaxation oscillator into a crude
but effective crystal oscillator. If R1 and C1 set the operating
frequency close to the crystal frequency, the crystal in effect
takes over, and oscillation occurs at the resonant frequency of
the crystal. The specified values for R1 and C1 are suitable
for a 1MHz crystal, but C1 should be made proportionately
lower in value for higher frequencies. A little experimentation
may be needed in order to find a value which gives reliable

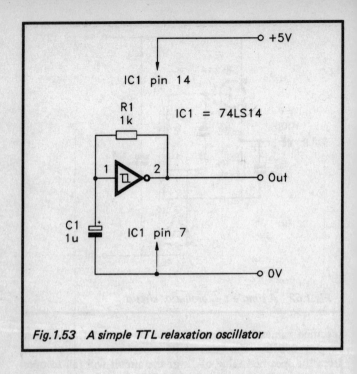

Fig.1.53 A simple TTL relaxation oscillator

operation at the crystal frequency. The circuit should work
at frequencies of up to at least 6MHz. This circuit shows
how a spare inverter of IC1 can be used to provide an anti-
phase not Q output.

One of the four Norton amplifiers in an LM3900N forms
the basis of the simple oscillator circuit of Figure 1.55. This
provides a roughly squarewave output, and is the Norton
amplifier equivalent to the standard operational amplifier
oscillator circuit of Figure 1.6. R4 and C1 are the timing
components, and with the specified values the circuit oscillates at about 1kHz. R4 should have a value in the range
10k to 100k. C1 can have any value of about 100p or more,
and can be a polarised type (with the positive terminal connected to R1 and R4). The circuit will operate up to a
frequency of at least 100kHz.

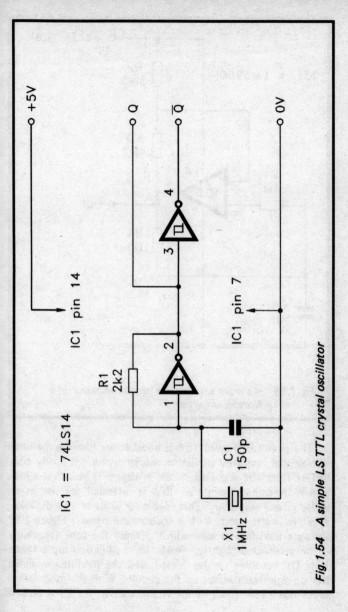

Fig.1.54 A simple LS TTL crystal oscillator

67

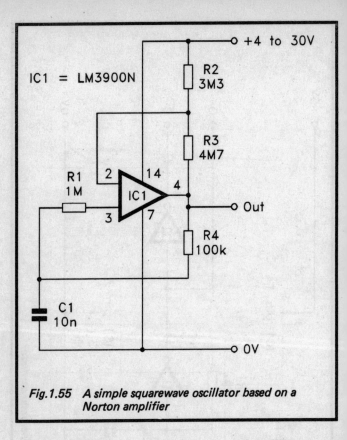

IC1 = LM3900N

R2 3M3
R3 4M7
R1 1M
R4 100k
+4 to 30V
Out
0V
2
14
4
IC1
3
7
C1 10n

*Fig.1.55   A simple squarewave oscillator based on a
Norton amplifier*

The circuit of Figure 1.56 is another variation on the basic
operational amplifier oscillator configuration. It really only
differs from the standard circuit in that it is based on a high
power operational amplifier that is intended for use as an
audio power amplifier. This enables it to drive a loudspeaker
at a few watts r.m.s. with a squarewave signal. Figure 1.57
shows a modified version which permits the tone frequency
to be modulated slightly. With the modulation input taken
high D1 becomes reverse biased, and the modulation signal
has no significant affect on the circuit. With the modulation
input taken low, some of the charge current for C3 is tapped

68

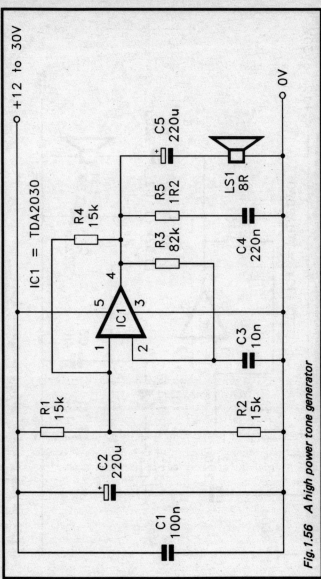

+12 to 30V

0V

IC1 = TDA2030

R4 15k

R1 15k

R2 15k

R3 82k

R5 1R2

C5 220u +

C4 220n

C3 10n

C2 220u +

C1 100n

LS1 8R

IC1

5
4
3
1
2

Fig. 1.56 A high power tone generator

69

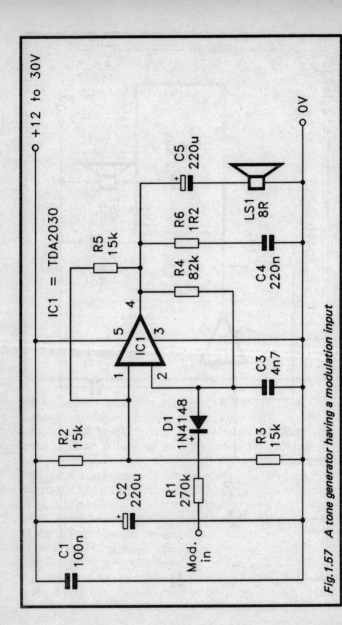

Fig. 1.57 A tone generator having a modulation input

70

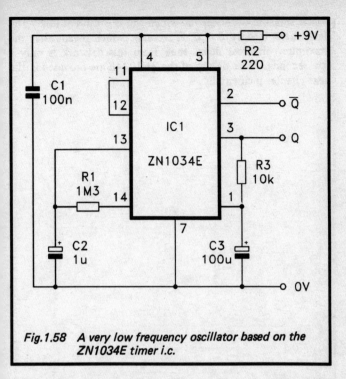

Fig.1.58 A very low frequency oscillator based on the ZN1034E timer i.c.

off through D1 and R1, giving a reduction in the output frequency. This switches the output frequency between approximately 1kHz and 2kHz, giving a good alarm signal. Note that IC1 must be fitted on at least a medium sized heatsink or it will overheat.

Figure 1.58 shows the circuit diagram for a very low frequency oscillator based on the ZN1034E timer integrated circuit. This is a complex device which includes a C − R oscillator, divider chain, and control logic. R1 and C2 are the timing components, and they give an output pulse that is some 2736 C R seconds. This works out at 3556.8 seconds with the specified values, or just under one hour in other words. The ZN1034E is basically a monostable multivibrator, but the circuit triggers and retriggers itself due to the coupling through R3 and C3. This is the secondary timing network which sets the duration for which the Q output is low. The delay here is only 0.6 C R seconds, which means that the maximum practical delay time from this network is only a few seconds. More details of the ZN1034E are provided in the next chapter incidentally.

Chapter 2

MONOSTABLES AND TIMERS

Monostables and other timing circuits are to be found in many electronic devices. The timing circuits in this chapter can provide output pulses from a few nanoseconds to more than a week in duration.

555 Monostables

The 555 is the obvious choice for most simple timing applications. Figure 2.1 shows the circuit for a basic 555 monostable. Like a 555 astable, the monostable configuration can place noise spikes onto the supply lines due to crowbarring during output transitions. Consequently, it is advisable to

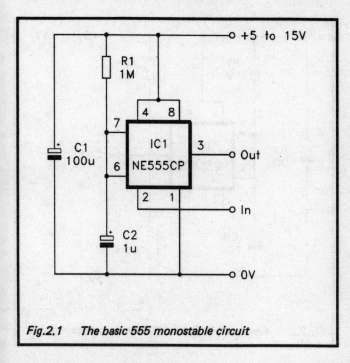

Fig.2.1   The basic 555 monostable circuit

include a sizeable supply decoupling capacitor (C1) in a 555 monostable circuit. The timing components are R1 and C2. The duration of the output pulse is equal to 1.1 C R seconds, or 1.1 seconds using the specified values. The output is a positive pulse incidentally, and a minimum pulse length of about 1 microsecond can be achieved.

An important point to bear in mind with a basic 555 monostable is that it can only operate as a pulse stretcher. The trigger signal must be a negative pulse which takes pin 2 below one-third of the supply voltage, and it must take pin 2 back above this threshold level before the end of the output pulse. Otherwise the output pulse will end when pin 2 is taken back above one-third of the supply voltage.

Manual triggering of a 555 monostable can be provided in the simple manner shown in Figure 2.2, but only where a fairly long output time is being provided (i.e. about 2 seconds or

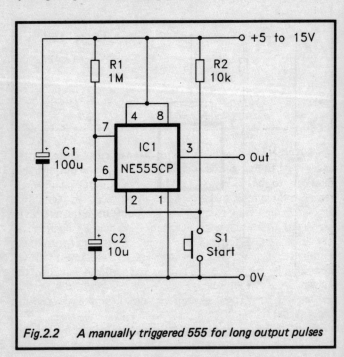

Fig.2.2   A manually triggered 555 for long output pulses

74

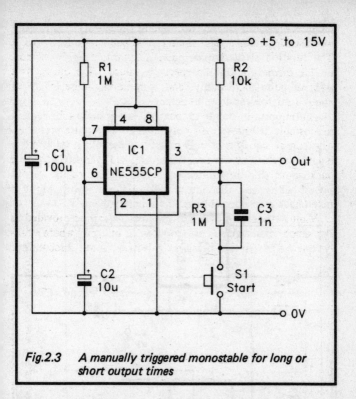

*Fig.2.3   A manually triggered monostable for long or
short output times*

more). There is then little risk of S1 still being closed at the
end of the timing period, which would cause the output pulse
duration to be increased.   Where short output pulses are
required the circuit of Figure 2.3 can be used. In fact this is
a good choice even when quite long output pulses are being
provided, as it ensures that someone keeping S1 pressed will
not cause a malfunction of the circuit. Operating S1 produces
a short trigger pulse as C3 charges via R2. Holding S1 closed
does not keep pin 2 of IC1 low, and will not lengthen the
output pulse. R3 discharges C3 when S1 is released, so that
the circuit is almost instantly ready to produce another
trigger pulse.
    The 555 has a reset input at pin 4. This pin is normally
tied to the positive supply rail, but it will reset the circuit

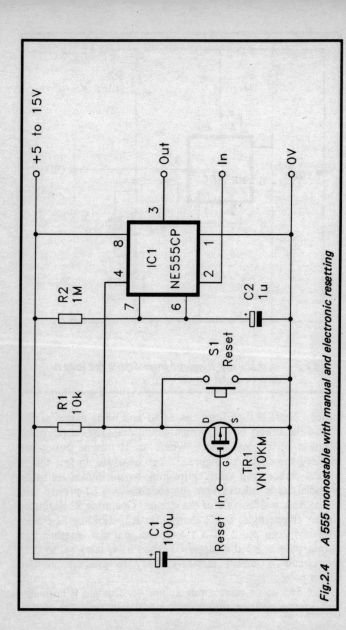

Fig.2.4   A 555 monostable with manual and electronic resetting

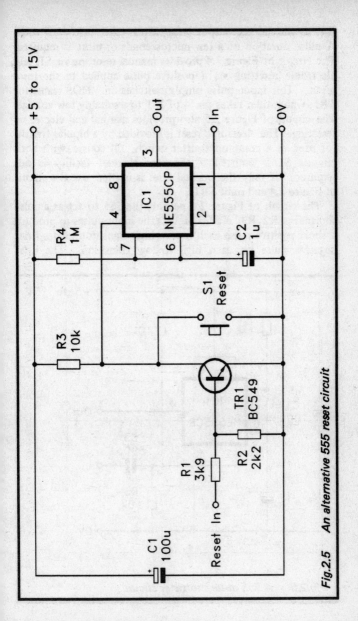

Fig.2.5 An alternative 555 reset circuit

77

(i.e. it will end the output pulse) if it is taken below 0.5 volts. A pulse duration of a few microseconds or more is required. The circuit of Figure 2.4 provides manual resetting via S1, and electronic resetting via a positive pulse applied to the reset input. This input pulse simply switches on VMOS transistor TR1, which then takes pin 4 of IC1 to a suitably low voltage. The circuit of Figure 2.5 also provides manual and electronic resetting. The electronic reset is provided by a bipolar transistor used as a common emitter switch. Of course, with both circuits S1 is omitted if the manual reset facility is not required. If only the manual reset is needed, use the circuit of Figure 2.4 and omit TR1.

The circuit of Figure 2.6 permits the 555 to act as a pulse shortener. R2, R3, and C3 process the input pulses to produce a short positive pulse each low to high transition, and a brief negative pulse on each high to low transition. The brief

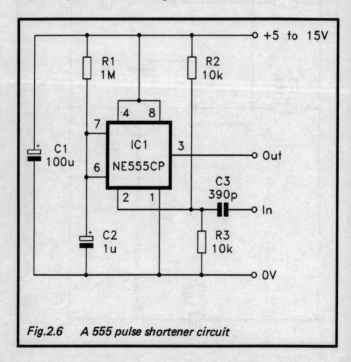

Fig.2.6   A 555 pulse shortener circuit

78

negative pulses trigger IC1. For this circuit to work properly the input pulses must be a few volts peak to peak in amplitude, and must also have reasonably fast switching times. Something like a low frequency sine or triangular input signal will not provide the desired result.

It can sometimes be useful to be able to trim the output pulse duration of a 555 monostable to precisely the required figure. Normally this would be accomplished by using a fixed resistor in series with a preset resistor for the timing resistance. However, suppose that (say) the timing resistor was a calibrated potentiometer giving a range of output pulse lengths. It would then be more than a little helpful to have a totally separate trimmer control to permit the range of actual output times to be matched with the required range of output times. This is possible, and requires a preset resistor to be connected to pin 5 of IC1, as shown in Figure 2.7. Normally the output

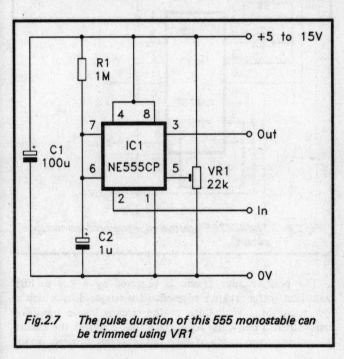

*Fig.2.7   The pulse duration of this 555 monostable can
be trimmed using VR1*

79

pulse ends when the charge on the timing capacitor reaches two-thirds of the supply voltage. VR1 can be used to pull this threshold level higher or lower, respectively giving increased and decreased output times.

4047BE Monostables

Like the 555, the CMOS 4047BE can be used in both astable and monostable modes. Its three monostable modes are the positive edge triggered, negative edge triggered, and retriggerable modes. The relevant circuits are shown in Figures 2.8 to 2.10 respectively.

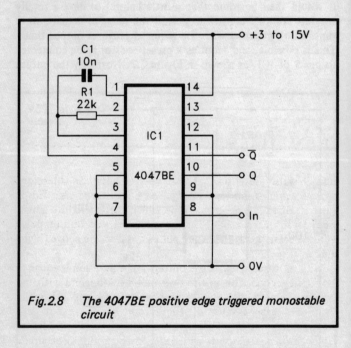

Fig.2.8   The 4047BE positive edge triggered monostable circuit

The positive edge circuit is triggered by a low to high transition — the negative edge circuit is triggered by a high to low transition. With both of the circuits it is a transition rather than a particular logic state that activates the circuit. Accordingly, the length of the input pulse has no affect on the

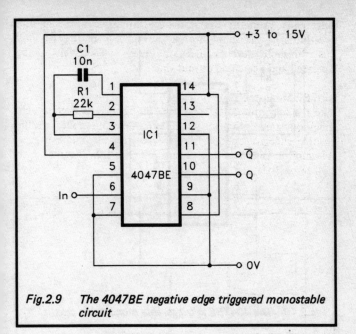

Fig.2.9 *The 4047BE negative edge triggered monostable circuit*

output pulse duration. These two circuits can therefore operate as pulse shorteners as well as pulse stretchers. This is not true of the retriggerable type which is triggered by a high input level. Like a basic 555 monostable, the output pulse will not cease while the input pulse is still at the active (high) state.

With all three circuits the output pulse duration is equal to 2.48 C R seconds (or a little over half a millisecond with the example values). R1 should be between 10k and 1M, while C1 should have a value of 1n or more. C1 can not be a polarised capacitor. The circuit seems to work with R1 at values of up to 10M, but with values over 1M timing accuracy might be lost.

CMOS Monostables

Monostables can be produced at low cost using CMOS gates, but it has to be pointed out that such a circuit will not

81

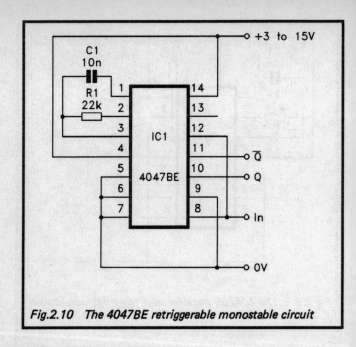

Fig.2.10   The 4047BE retriggerable monostable circuit

provide the same degree of timing accuracy as a circuit based
on the 4047BE. Figure 2.11 shows the circuit diagram for a
basic CMOS monostable.   This is a non-retriggerable type
which is positive edge triggered and provides a positive output
pulse.   C1 and R1 are the timing components, and the pulse
duration is roughly equal to 0.65 C R seconds (or about one
second using the specified values).   C1 can have any value of
more than about 30p, and if necessary it can be a polarised
type.   R1 can have any value from about 10k to many
megohms.

One slight problem with the basic monostable circuit is
that the output tends to switch relatively slowly at the end of
the output pulse, particularly with long output pulses.   The
circuit of Figure 2.12 gives better results by using the two
previously unused gates of IC1 as an amplifier to speed up the
fall time of the output pulse.   This also has the advantage of
providing a not Q output.

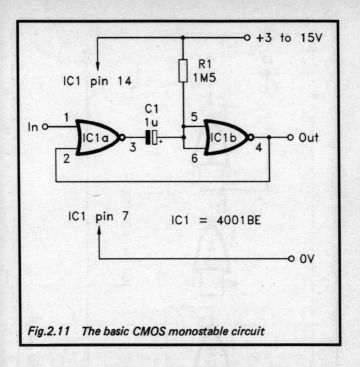

Fig.2.11   The basic CMOS monostable circuit

The slightly revamped CMOS monostable of Figure 2.13 has similar characteristics to the original circuit. However, it is negative edge triggered monostable, whereas the original circuit is a positive edge triggered type.

Where a TTL compatible monostable is required a circuit based on the 555 may well be suitable, since this device has a TTL compatible output. Where a fully TTL compatible monostable is needed a circuit based on the 74121 is likely to be a better choice. Triggering the 74121 is something less than straightforward because it has a couple of gates ahead of the trigger input. It therefore has to be triggered via these gates. However, things can be rationalised to produce basic positive and negative edge triggered monostables (Figures 2.14 and 2.15 respectively). The positive edge triggered circuit has a Schmitt trigger input stage, and consequently it will trigger reliably from slow input signals. In both circuits R1

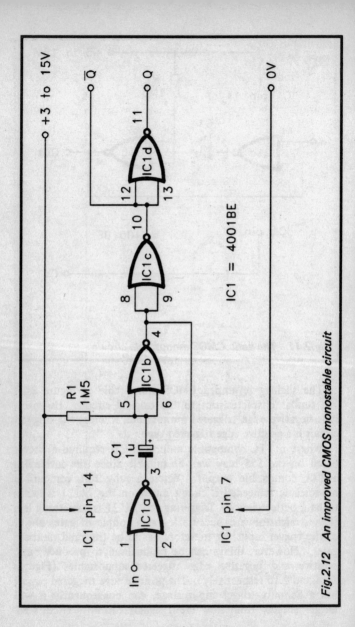

Fig.2.12 An improved CMOS monostable circuit

+3 to 15V

Q̄

Q

0V

IC1 pin 14

IC1 pin 7

In

IC1a
1
2

C1
1u
3

R1
1M5
5

IC1b
6
4

IC1c
8
9
10

IC1d
12
13
11

IC1 = 4001BE

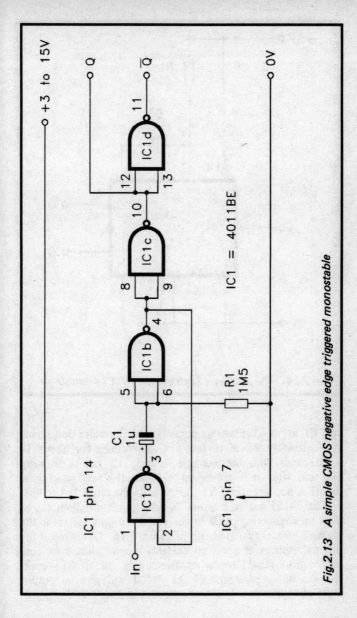

Fig.2.13   A simple CMOS negative edge triggered monostable

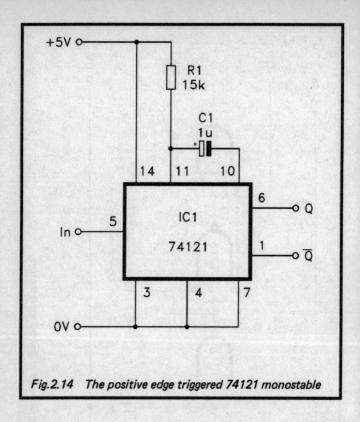

Fig.2.14 The positive edge triggered 74121 monostable

and C1 are the timing components, and the pulse duration is approximately equal to 0.695 C R seconds (or about 10 milliseconds with the example values). C1 can be between 10p and 10μ, or it can be up to 1000μ if a very rapid pulse cutoff is not essential. R1 should be in the range 1k4 to 40k.

The 74121 has an internal 2k timing resistor which can be used by connecting pin 9 to the positive supply rail, as in the positive edge triggered circuit of Figure 2.16. Of course, if the internal resistor is used, no external resistor should be connected from pin 11 to the positive supply rail. If C1 is omitted the self capacitance of the 74121 will give an output pulse of approximately 30 nanoseconds in duration.

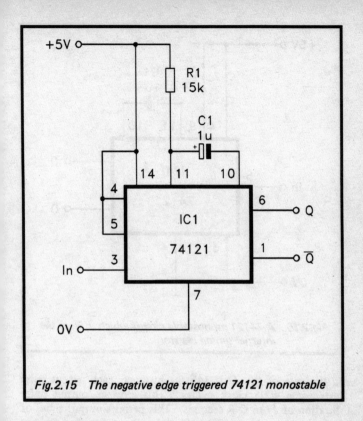

Fig.2.15 The negative edge triggered 74121 monostable

Precision Timers

There is a limit to the practical pulse times available using simple C – R timing circuits. Even using high value timing components such as a 100μ capacitor and a 10M resistor, the pulse duration obtained would typically be only about 18 minutes or so. In reality it is unlikely that such high values would actually work properly, since the leakage through the capacitor would probably equal the charge current through the resistor, giving an indefinite output pulse duration.

Precision timers overcome this problem by using a C – R oscillator and a long divider chain. The duration of the output pulse is equal to a certain number of clock pulses, and

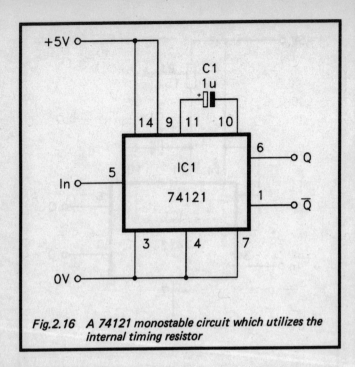

Fig.2.16 A 74121 monostable circuit which utilizes the internal timing resistor

in the case of the ZN1034E for instance, each output pulse lasts some 4095 clock cycles. This gives an output pulse duration of 2736 C R seconds. This permits output times of hours or even days to be achieved without the need for any impractically high timing component values.

Figure 2.17 shows the circuit diagram for a simple precision long timer based on the ZN1034E. The circuit triggers at switch-on as its negative trigger input (pin 1) is wired to the 0 volt supply rail. If desired, this can be held high by a resistor of a few kilohms in value and pulsed low to trigger the circuit. Figure 2.18 shows the circuit for a ZN1034E timer which has manual triggering via this method. The ZN1034E can also be triggered by a negative logic pulse on its TTL compatible trigger input.

R1 and C2 are the timing components. The specified values give an output pulse duration of a little under ten hours! R1

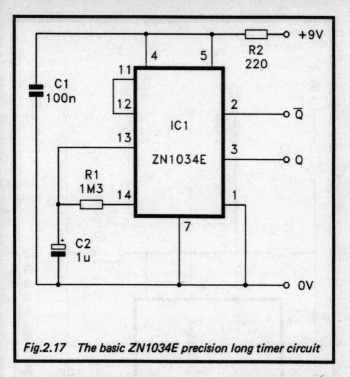

Fig.2.17   The basic ZN1034E precision long timer circuit

can have any value of between about 3k3 and 5M. C1 can have any value from 3n3 upwards, and if necessary it can be a polarised component. Q and not Q outputs are available, both of which are TTL compatible.

The ZN1034E includes a simple 5 volt regulator, and R2 is the load resistor for this shunt type regulator. For supply potentials of 6, 12, 15, and 24 volts the value of R2 should be 56R, 390R, 560R, and 1k2 respectively. If the circuit is used on a 5 volt supply R2 should be replaced by a shorting link, and pin 5 should be left unconnected.

The circuit of Figure 2.19 includes a calibration preset (VR1) which enables the output pulse duration to be trimmed. This preset is in series with an internal resistor, and it permits the pulse length to be varied from 2736 C R seconds at minimum resistance, to about 4095 C R seconds at maximum

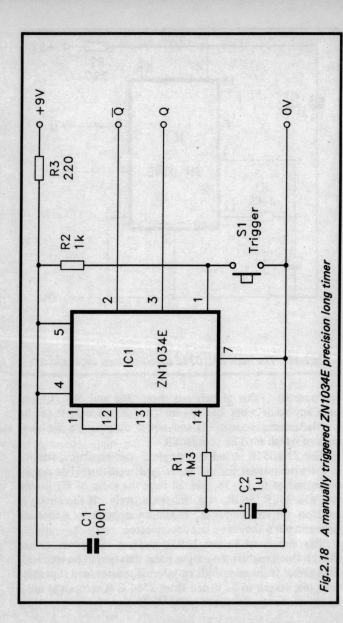

Fig.2.18 A manually triggered ZN1034E precision long timer

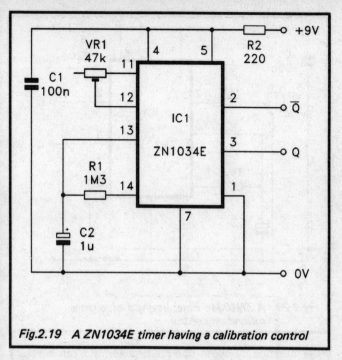

Fig.2.19 A ZN1034E timer having a calibration control

resistance. In the circuit of Figure 2.20 the internal calibration resistor is left unused, and the calibration resistance is provided by discrete components VR1 and R1. This permits a wider calibration range to be covered. The pulse duration is about 2500 C R seconds with VR1 at minimum resistance, to around 7500 C R seconds with it at maximum value. Note that for optimum stability no external calibration resistance should be used.

Figure 2.21 shows the circuit diagram for a triggered sawtooth generator circuit. This is basically a 555 monostable, but the timing resistance is provided by a constant current generator. The timing capacitor (C1) therefore charges at a constant rate, producing a linear ramp waveform across C1. As this signal is at a high impedance it is taken via a buffer amplifier (IC1). The timing resistor is effectively R3, and the example values for R3 and C1 gives an output

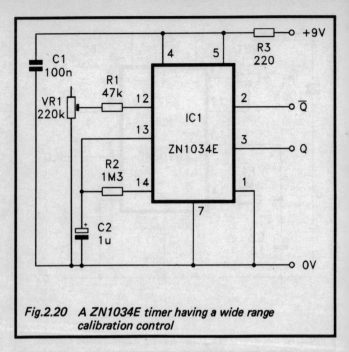

Fig.2.20 A ZN1034E timer having a wide range calibration control

pulse duration of about one millisecond. R3 can have any value from about 56R to around 1M.

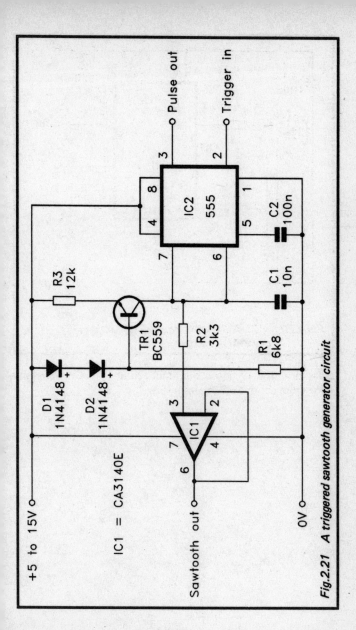

Fig.2.21 A triggered sawtooth generator circuit

93

Chapter 3

DIGITAL CIRCUITS

In this chapter a number of digital circuits, such as dividers, counters, decoders, and analogue converters are described. Oscillators and monostables for use in digital circuits are not considered in any detail as both types of circuit are covered in the previous two chapters.

1 of 10 Decoder

The CMOS 4017BE is an extremely versatile decoder and divider integrated circuit. It is a good choice where a simple divide by ten action is required, and Figure 3.1 shows the necessary connections for this mode of operation. Pin 15 is the reset input, and it is taken high to reset IC1. However, in most simple divide by ten applications this facility will not

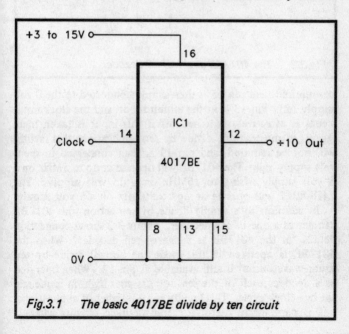

Fig.3.1   The basic 4017BE divide by ten circuit

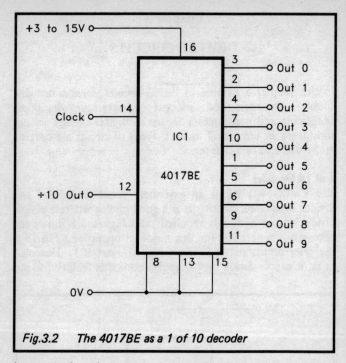

Fig.3.2   The 4017BE as a 1 of 10 decoder

be required, and pin 15 is then simply connected to the 0 volt supply rail. Pin 13 is in the inhibit input, and the clock input signal is effectively switched off if this input is taken high. Again, in most simple divide by ten applications this facility will not be required, and pin 13 is then connected to the 0 volt supply rail. The 4017BE will operate at up to 5MHz on a 5 volt supply, rising to 16MHz on a 15 volt supply. The 74HC4017 will operate at up to 50MHz on a 5 volt supply.

In addition to a simple divide by ten action, the 4017BE can act as a one of ten decoder. Figure 3.2 shows connection details for the 4017BE as a one of ten decoder. When the 4017BE is operated in this mode the normal divide by ten squarewave output is still available at pin 12. When operated as a decoder each of the ten outputs goes high, in sequence, for one clock cycle. This facility has a number of applications, but is particularly useful for control logic circuits where a

96

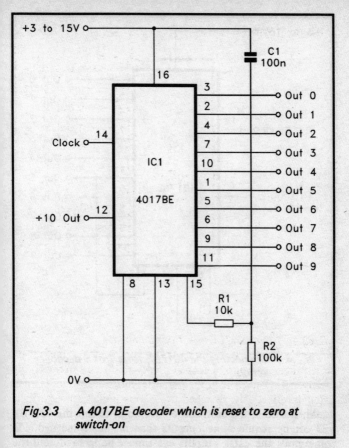

Fig.3.3   A 4017BE decoder which is reset to zero at switch-on

sequence of events must be made to happen in the right order.

When used in this manner it is often important that the counter starts from zero at switch-on. This can be accomplished using a simple C – R timing circuit connected to the reset input, as shown in Figure 3.3. In some cases quite a long reset pulse might be needed, so that the other stages in the circuit have time to settle at their normal operating conditions. A longer reset pulse can be obtained by making C1 and (or) R2 higher in value.

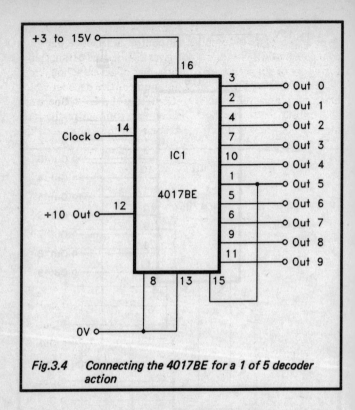

Fig.3.4 Connecting the 4017BE for a 1 of 5 decoder action

When used as the basis of a control logic circuit the 4017BE will often provide more outputs than are really needed. In some cases the extra outputs can simply be ignored, and the "dead" states that this will introduce into the control sequence will not matter. However, this will not always be the case, and in most instances it would be preferable to remove the "dead" states. This is easily accomplished, and it is just a matter of getting the 4017BE to reset itself at the end of each sequence (Fig.3.4). In this example the reset input (pin 15) is connected to output 5. Therefore, the circuit operates normally at first, with outputs 0, 1, 2, 3, and 4 all going high in sequence. However, as soon as output 5 goes high the circuit resets itself, and the count continues from zero again. This effectively eliminates outputs 5 to 9, and gives a one of five decoder. Of course, in practice pin 15 is connected to whichever output gives the desired action (pin 6 for a one of six action, pin 7 for a one of seven action, etc.).

The circuit of Figure 3.5 is for a one of five decoder which has a switch-on reset facility. Obviously the C − R network and output 5 can not both be connected direct to the reset input. For the circuit to work correctly they must feed the

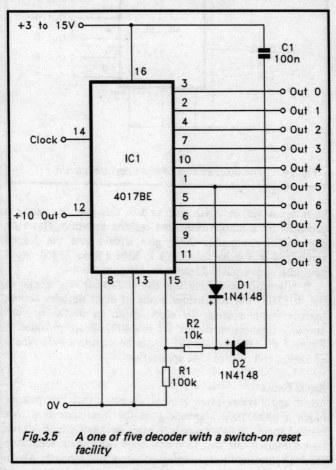

Fig.3.5   A one of five decoder with a switch-on reset
            facility

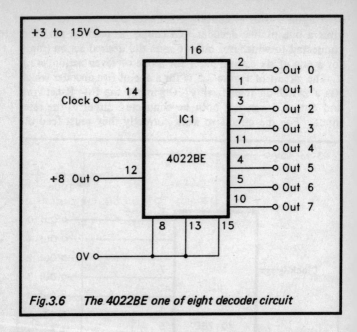

Fig.3.6   The 4022BE one of eight decoder circuit

reset input via an AND gate, and in this case the gating is provided by a simple diode and resistor network. However, any CMOS compatible AND gate should give the desired result, and it is quite acceptable to have a three or four input gate with each input fed from a separate source.

It is worth mentioning that the 4022BE is very similar to the 4017BE, but it provides a one of eight decoder action, together with a divide by eight action on its "carry out" output. Connection details for the 4022BE are provided in Figure 3.6. Like the 4017BE it can be used in a wide variety of divider and control logic applications.

Signal Gates

Logic applications often require a circuit that can pass or block a pulse train, depending on the logic state feed to a control input. In other words, a basic logic gate circuit. It has to be pointed out that in many cases there is no need for a separate gate circuit, since many counters, dividers, etc., have a

100

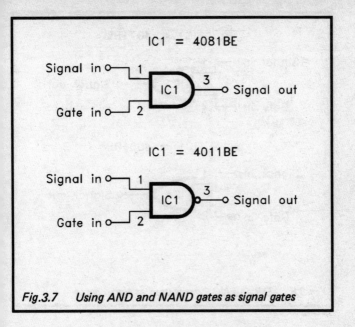

Fig.3.7   Using AND and NAND gates as signal gates

gate input of some kind (the "inhibit" input of the 4017BE for example).

Figure 3.7 shows how AND and NAND gates can be used to provide a simple signal gate action. In both cases the input signal is coupled through to the output when the gate input is high, and blocked when it is low. Note that with a NAND gate the input signal appears inverted at the output. In Figure 3.8 OR and NOR gates are used as signal gates. These enable the input signal to pass through to the output when the gate input is low, and block the signal when it is high. The NOR gate provides an inversion from the signal input to the output.

Dividers

We have already seen how the 4017BE and 4022BE can be used to provide divide by ten and divide by eight actions, but there are many other divider integrated circuits. The 4018BE is one of the most versatile of these divider chips. It can be

101

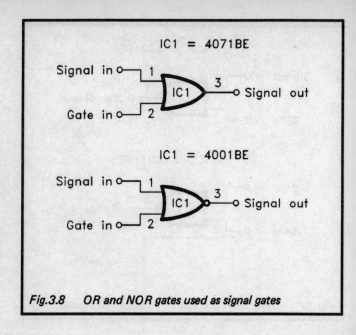

Fig.3.8   OR and NOR gates used as signal gates

wired to provide division rates of two, four, six, eight, or ten, as shown in Figure 3.9. S1 is used to select the desired division rate, but obviously IC1 can be hard wired for the required division rate in applications where only one rate is required.   The 4018BE will operate at up to 2.5MHz on a 5 volt supply, rising to 8MHz on a 15 volt supply.

For a simple divide by two action a D type flip/flop can be used. This provides a divide by two action if its not Q output is coupled back to the data input. Figure 3.10 shows the connections needed to make a CMOS 4013BE dual D type flip/flop act as a simple divide by two counter. In Figure 3.11 both flip/flops are used and are connected in series to give a divide by four action. The 4013BE will operate with input frequencies of up to 4MHz when it is run from a 5 volt supply, or 14MHz when it is powered from a 15 volt supply.

For higher division rates there are a number of devices which offer between seven and fourteen stages of binary division (i.e. division rates of between 128 and 16384). One

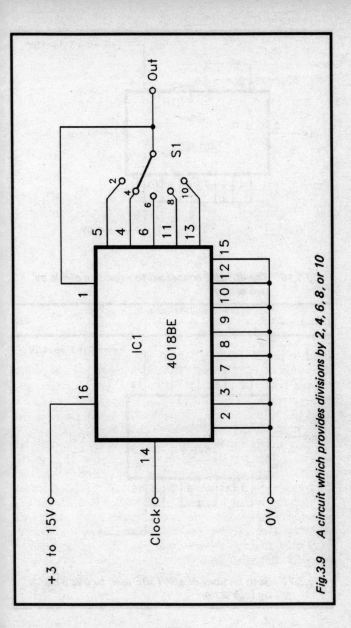

Fig.3.9   A circuit which provides divisions by 2, 4, 6, 8, or 10

103

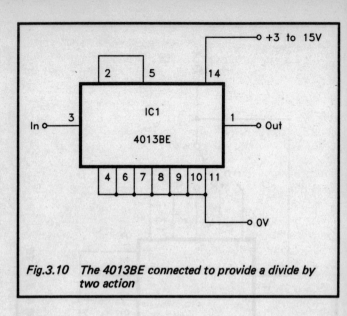

Fig.3.10 The 4013BE connected to provide a divide by two action

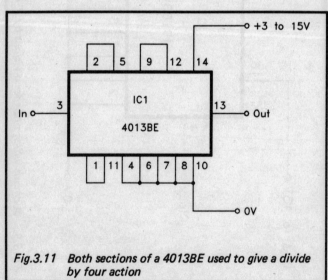

Fig.3.11 Both sections of a 4013BE used to give a divide by four action

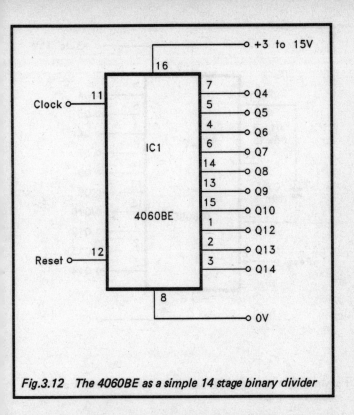

Fig.3.12   The 4060BE as a simple 14 stage binary divider

of the most useful of these is the CMOS 4060BE. This has
two inverters at the input which can be used as the basis of a
C – R oscillator or a crystal type. The binary divider chain
has fourteen stages, but the outputs of stages one, two, three,
and eleven are not available externally. Consequently, with
this device division rates of two, four, eight, and 2048 are not
available.   The 4060BE will operate at up to 5MHz with a
5 volt supply, rising to 17MHz with a 15 volt supply.

Figure 3.12 shows connection details for a basic 4060BE
binary divider. The circuit of Figure 3.13 uses the two
inverters at the input as a simple C – R clock oscillator, which
uses the configuration that was described in Chapter 1 (see
Figure 1.39 and the accompanying text).   The circuit of

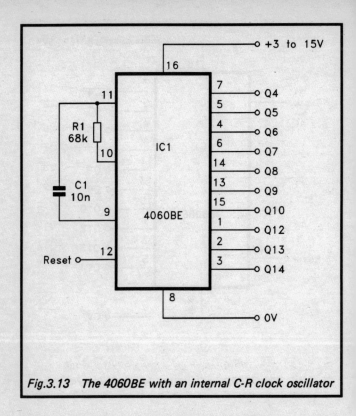

Fig.3.13   The 4060BE with an internal C-R clock oscillator

Figure 3.14 uses one of the inverters as a simple crystal oscillator. This is again an oscillator configuration that was described in Chapter 1 (see Figure 1.48 and the accompanying text).

The 4060BE has a reset input at pin 12, but in most applications this will probably not be required, and is then simply wired to the negative supply rail. Figure 3.15 shows the circuit for a 4060BE divider which has a C − R network to provide a reset pulse at switch-on.

As with any divider circuits, 4060BEs can be connected in series in order to obtain higher division rates and more output frequencies. In fact it is sometimes necessary to use a combination of binary, decade, and divide by "N" circuits in

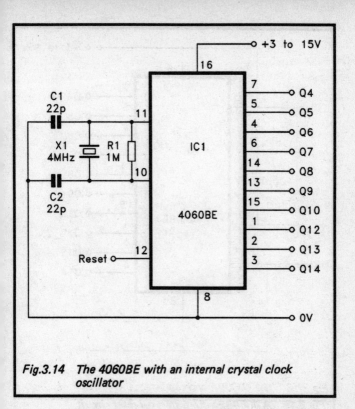

Fig.3.14 *The 4060BE with an internal crystal clock oscillator*

order to obtain the desired division rate or rates. Figure 3.16 gives connection details for two 4060BEs wired in series. It is just a matter of connecting the final output of one device to the clock input of the next one in the chain.

The 4024BE is a useful device which provides seven stages of binary division. All seven outputs are available externally, as can be seen from Figure 3.17 which provides connection details for the 4024BE. This device will operate at clock frequencies of up to 2.5MHz with a 5 volt supply, or 12MHz with a 15 volt supply. The 74HC4024 will operate at up to 70MHz on a 5 volt supply.

The 4020BE is a 14 stage binary divider, but the outputs of stages two and three are not externally accessible. This device

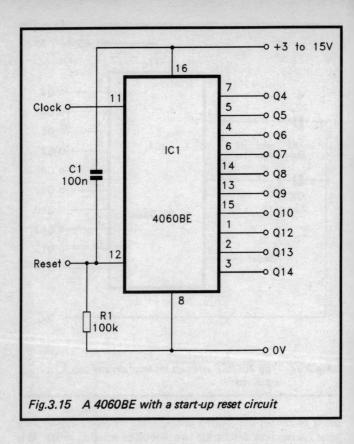

Fig.3.15 A 4060BE with a start-up reset circuit

has a Schmitt trigger input stage. It will operate with input frequencies of up to 3.5MHz when it is operated from a 5 volt supply, rising to 13MHz when using a 15 volt supply. The 74HC4020 will operate at up to 40MHz using a 5 volt supply. Connection details for the 4020BE are shown in Figure 3.18.

The 4040BE is a 12 stage binary divider which has all twelve outputs available. It will operate at input frequencies of up to 2.1MHz using a 5 volt supply, or 10MHz using 15 volt supply. The 74HC4040 will operate at up to 40MHz on a 5 volt supply. Connection details for the 4040BE are provided in Figure 3.19.

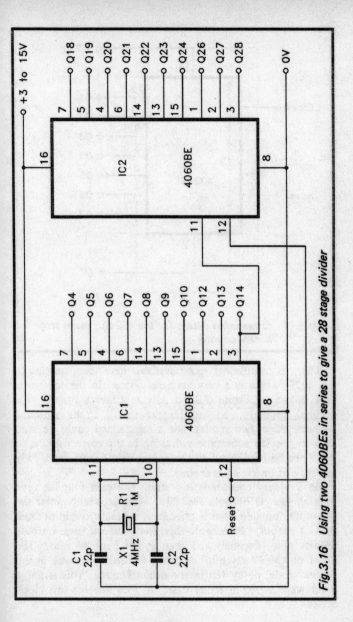

Fig.3.16 Using two 4060BEs in series to give a 28 stage divider

109

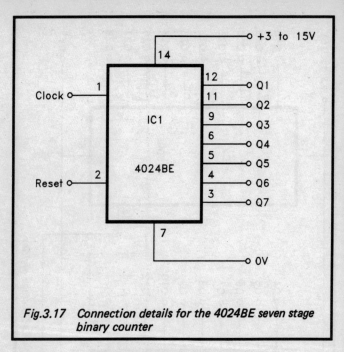

Fig.3.17 Connection details for the 4024BE seven stage binary counter

There is insufficient space available here to do justice to the 4029, which is a very versatile device. In the configuration shown in Figure 3.20 it acts as either a binary or a decimal counter. S1 enables the circuit to be switched between these two modes, but a logic signal could be used here to provide automatic switching to the correct mode, or pin 9 can be hard wired to the appropriate supply rail if only one type of operation is needed.

As a binary counter it is a straightforward four bit type with all four Q outputs available. As a decimal counter the Q outputs provide what is effectively a binary coded decimal (b.c.d.) output. In other words, the value on these outputs reaches nine (decimal) and then cycles back to zero. The signal on the "carry out" output is divided by sixteen in the binary mode, or by ten in the decimal mode. This is not a squarewave signal in either case. It goes low for one clock cycle.

110

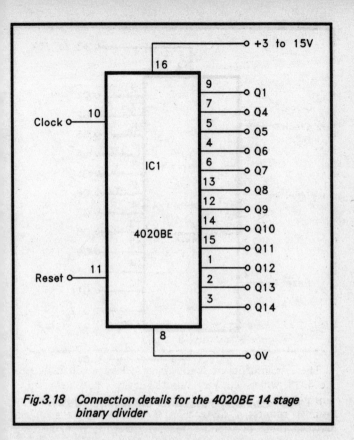

Fig.3.18   Connection details for the 4020BE 14 stage binary divider

Figure 3.21 provides connection details for using the 4029BE as a down counter (i.e. it counts repeatedly from 9 down to 0, not 0 up to 9). This circuit is basically the same as the up counter, but pin 10 is connected to the negative supply rail whereas it was previously connected to the positive supply rail. In either mode the 4029BE will operate with input frequencies of up to 4MHz when it is operated from a 5 volt supply, or 10MHz if a 15 volt supply is used.

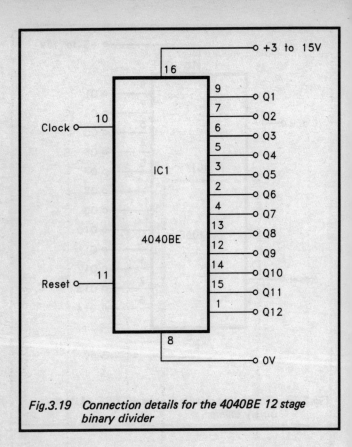

Fig.3.19 Connection details for the 4040BE 12 stage binary divider

Display Drivers

Figure 3.22 shows the circuit for a decoder/driver that will convert a binary coded decimal input to the appropriate digit displayed on a seven segment display (e.g. 0011 on the input will cause a "3" to be displayed). R1 to R7 provide current limiting on the outputs of IC1. With low supply voltages of about 5 volts a slightly lower value (about 330R) would be advisable as the specified value might give rather low display brightness. At high supply voltages of about 12 to 15 volts a higher value (about 1k) is preferable, as the l.e.d. current might otherwise be excessive. No type number is given for the

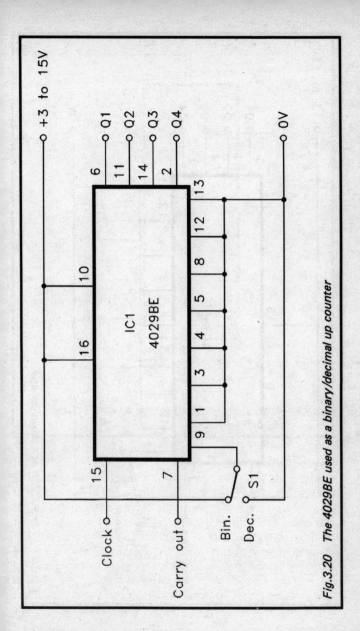

Fig.3.20 The 4029BE used as a binary/decimal up counter

113

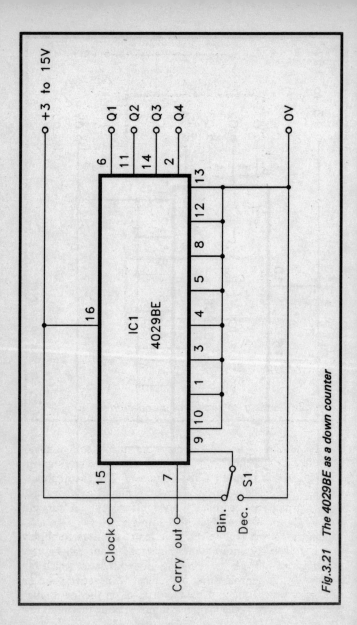

Fig.3.21 The 4029BE as a down counter

114

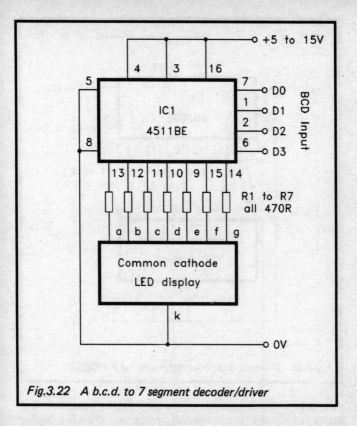

Fig.3.22   A b.c.d. to 7 segment decoder/driver

display because these days displays are mainly sold as something like a "0.5 inch l.e.d. common cathode seven segment display", rather than by a type number. The circuit should work well using any seven segment common cathode l.e.d. display which has reasonably good efficiency. It can not drive l.c.d. or common anode l.e.d. displays.

Pin 5 is shown as simply connecting to the negative supply rail, but in some applications this strobe input can be very useful. The 4511BE has a built-in four bit latch which can be used by having pin 5 normally high. A negative pulse on this input latches the four bit input signal on the low to high transition. Pin 3 is the lamp test input. Taking this input low

115

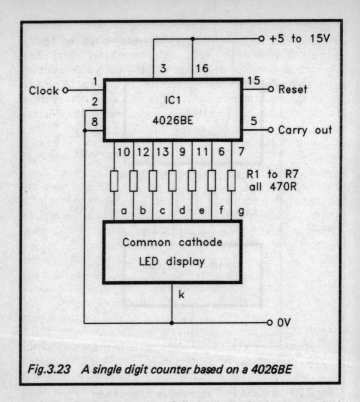

Fig.3.23   A single digit counter based on a 4026BE

results in all seven segments of the l.e.d. display being switched
on (a facility that is not normally required). Pin 4 is a display
blanking input which has the opposite effect. Taking this
input low results in all the segments of the display being
switched off.

The circuit of Figure 3.23 is for a single digit counter based
on a CMOS 4026BE decade counter and seven segment
decoder/driver. Like the previous circuit, this one has R1 to
R7 to provide current limiting on the outputs to the common
cathode l.e.d. display. The "Reset" pulsed is taken high in
order to reset the counter to zero. The displayed count then
advances by one each time a pulse is received on the clock
input. Pin 3 of IC1 is the display enable input, and this is
taken to the positive supply rail for normal operation. Taking

116

this input low results in the display being blanked. This input plus a suitable control circuit can be used to blank the display during the counting process, with the display only being switched on once the count has finished and a stable display is available. There is a gate input at pin 2 which can be used to switch the clock input signal on and off. This input is taken low to permit normal operation, or high to inhibit the clocking action.

The 4026BE has a "carry out" output, and this can be connected to the clock input of the next counter in a multi-digit counter. Figure 3.24 for instance, shows the circuit for a three digit counter based on 4026BEs. You can have any number of counter stages "chained" together using this basic method of connection. The 4026BE will operate with clock frequencies of up to 5MHz if it is used with a 5 volt supply, rising to 16MHz if it is operated from a 15 volt supply.

The 4033BE is very similar to the 4026BE, but provides slightly different functions. Figure 3.25 shows the basic method of connection for a 4033BE. Pin 2 is a clock inhibit input, as on the 4026BE. Pin 3 is the ripple blanking input, and for normal operation this is tied to the positive supply rail. If leading zero suppression is required this input should be connected to the ripple blanking output (pin 4) of the previous 4033BE in the counter chain. Pin 14 is the lamp test input, and for normal operation this is connected to the 0 volt supply rail. Taking this input high results in all the segments of the display being switched on. The 4033BE can operate with input frequencies of up to 5MHz if it is used on a 5 volt supply, or 16MHz if it is operated from a 15 volt supply.

Probably the most useful of the CMOS counter/display driver chips is the 40110BE, which uses the basic method of connection shown in Figure 3.26. This chip is more versatile due to the inclusion of a built-in latch circuit, and its ability to operate as a down counter. In the circuit of Figure 3.26 it operates as an up counter. The count can proceed when the gate input is low, but is "frozen" when this input is taken high.

The circuit of Figure 3.27 is the down counter equivalent of Figure 3.26. This has a "borrow out" output in place of an up counter's "carry out" output, but in a multi-digit counter this is used in exactly the same way as a "carry out" output.

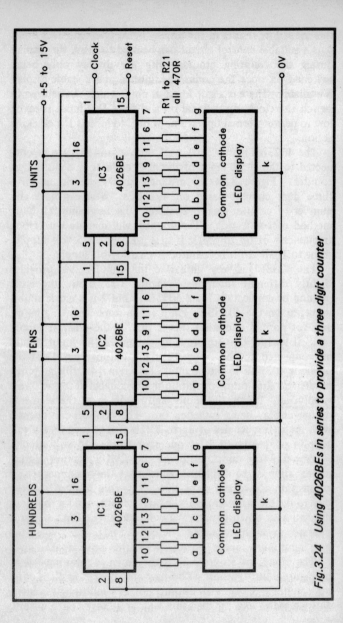

Fig.3.24 Using 4026BEs in series to provide a three digit counter

118

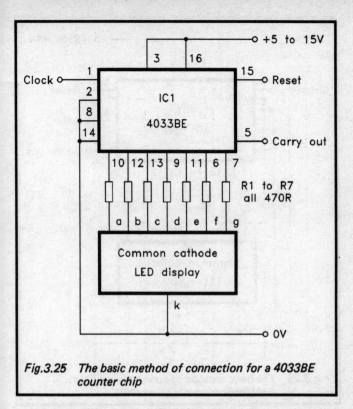

Fig.3.25 *The basic method of connection for a 4033BE counter chip*

In Figure 3.28 the 40110 counts continuously, but the display can be latched. With the "latch" input taken low the display will show the current counter value. However, if "latch" is taken high the display is "frozen", but the count will continue. In many applications both the gating and latch facilities will be required. The "latch" input is held high so that the previous reading is held on the display. The reset input is then pulsed high to reset the counter to zero, and the gate is taken low for the appropriate period so that a new count is taken. Finally, the "latch" input is pulsed low so that the new counter value is shown on the display. In this way a constant display can be obtained, with no blanking period while a new count is taken.

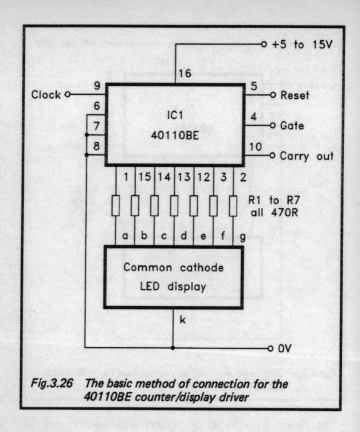

Fig.3.26 The basic method of connection for the 40110BE counter/display driver

The 40110BE has the unusual feature of being able to operate simultaneously as an up counter and a down type. This is possible since it has separate up and down clock input terminals, rather than one clock input and another pin to select the required mode of operation. Furthermore, as it also has separate "borrow out" and "carry out" outputs, it can be used in multi-digit up/down counters. Figure 3.29 provides connection details for the 40110BE as an up/down counter. In either mode of operation the 40110BE can operate at up to 2.5MHz on a 5 volt supply, rising to 8MHz on a 15 volt supply.

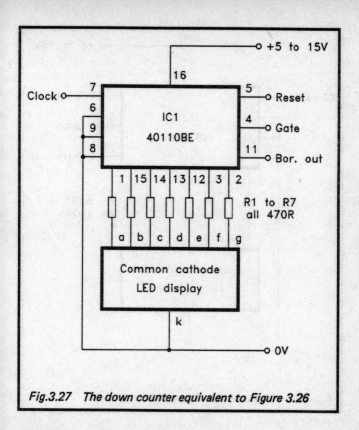

Fig.3.27 The down counter equivalent to Figure 3.26

Decoders

With digital circuits it is often necessary to have a circuit which will decode a set of inputs to a particular combination of input levels. In other words, with one particular set of input logic levels the output of the circuit will go to one logic state — with any other combination of input levels it will go to the other logic state. An address decoder in a computer add-on is an obvious example of a logic decoder circuit, but they are needed in many other applications.

One simple approach to the problem is to use a 74LS30 8 input NAND gate plus some inverters, as in the example circuit of Figure 3.30. The output of a NAND gate is low if

121

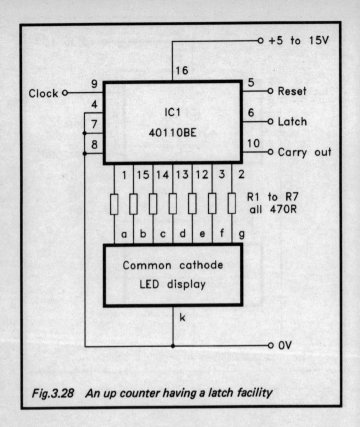

Fig.3.28   An up counter having a latch facility

all the inputs are high, or high for any other set of input
states. Obviously it will not normally be necessary to detect
all the inputs going high, but an input can be made to detect
a low input level simply by adding an inverter ahead of it.
Any unused inputs should be connected to the +5 volt supply
rail. In this way the circuit can detect any combination of
input levels, with up to eight input lines. In the example
circuit of Figure 3.30 the output is low unless the logic levels
fed to inputs 0 to 7 are 10101010 respectively. The inverters
are shown as being from a 74LS14 hex trigger/inverter device,
but any LS TTL inverters will suffice. Simply add an inverter

122

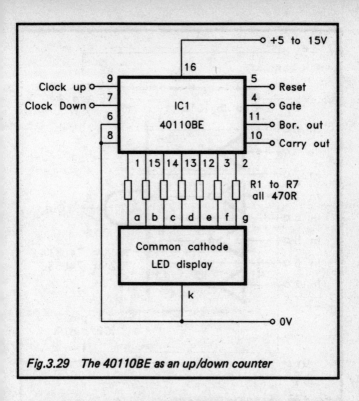

Fig.3.29   The 40110BE as an up/down counter

at the output if a high output level is required when the correct set of input states is detected.

A very different approach is used for the decoder circuit of Figure 3.31. This is based on a CMOS 4063BE 4 bit magnitude comparator, or for a TTL circuit a 74LS85 can be used. These two chips use exactly the same pin numbering, and provide precisely the same function. Of course, the 74LS85 should only be used with a 5 volt supply. In use the input lines to be decoded are connected to the "A" set of inputs, while the "B" set of inputs are hard-wired to the set of logic levels that must be decoded. There are three outputs available. It is normally pin 6 that is required, and this goes high when the correct binary input value is detected. Pin 7 goes high if the binary value on the "A" inputs is less than that

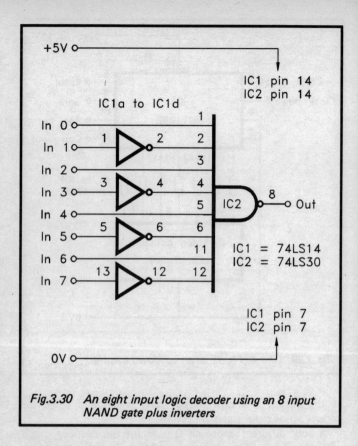

Fig.3.30 An eight input logic decoder using an 8 input NAND gate plus inverters

on the "B" inputs. Pin 5 goes high if the binary value on the "A" inputs is greater than that on the "B" inputs.

It is possible to cascade 4063BEs so that more than 4 bits can be decoded. Figure 3.32 shows the correct method of connection for two cascaded 4063BEs. It is basically just a matter of connecting the three outputs of the first device to the corresponding cascade inputs (pins 2, 3, and 4) of the second. This basic method of connection can be extended to any number of 4063s, but it is as well to remember that the 4063BE is not a particularly fast device. Cascading several of these chips results in the propagation delays being added

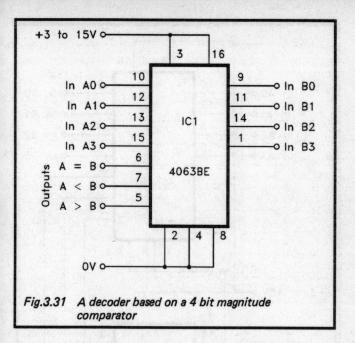

Fig.3.31   A decoder based on a 4 bit magnitude comparator

together, giving even slower operation. For high speed operation the 74LS85 must be used.

When decoding up to eight inputs the 74LS684 8 bit magnitude comparator offers a simple and fast alternative to a pair of cascaded 74LS85s. Figure 3.33 shows connection details for the 74LS684. The output from pin 19 goes low when the binary value on the "P" inputs is identical to that on the "Q" inputs. There is actually another output from pin 1 of IC1. This goes low when the binary value on the "P" inputs is greater than that on the "Q" inputs. However, it is the output from pin 19 that is required in most applications.

In some decoder applications it can be very useful to have an input state selector, so that the decoded value can be quickly altered. This is easily achieved using a magnitude comparator, and all that is needed is a simple switch circuit on the reference inputs instead of hard-wiring them to a certain set of logic states. Figure 3.34 shows an input selector

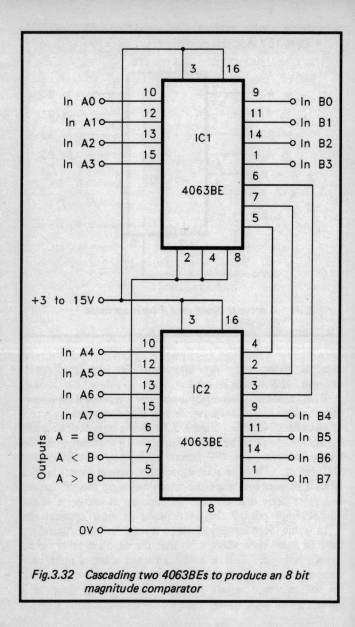

Fig.3.32 Cascading two 4063BEs to produce an 8 bit magnitude comparator

126

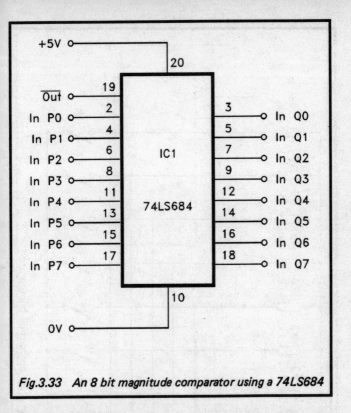

Fig.3.33   An 8 bit magnitude comparator using a 74LS684

for use with an 8 bit magnitude comparator, such as the circuit
of Figure 3.33.   Switches S1 to S8 select the decoded states
of inputs P0 to P7 respectively.   An input is decoded to the
low state if the corresponding switch is closed, or to a high
state if it is left open.

In and Outs

Often in digital circuits it is necessary to "grab" data which
will only be present on the output lines for a minute fraction
of a second.   A computer output port is a good example of
this.   The required data will probably be present on the data
bus for less than a microsecond, and during this period a pulse
will be produced from the address decoder circuit.   This pulse

127

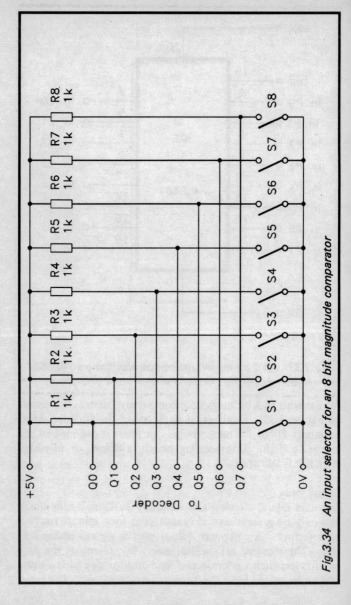

Fig.3.34 An input selector for an 8 bit magnitude comparator

128

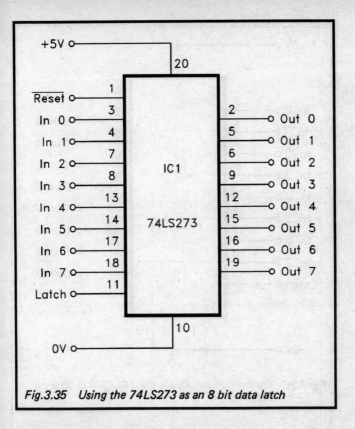

Fig.3.35 Using the 74LS273 as an 8 bit data latch

must be used to activate a data latch which will then hold the
data indefinitely.

There are numerous TTL devices which can act as data
latches. One of the most popular for this application is the
74LS273, which is an octal D type flip/flop. However, it will
function as an eight bit data latch if the pulse from the address
decoder (or whatever) is fed to the clock pulse input at pin 11.
The eight bit input signal connects to the data inputs, and
the bytes of latched data are available on the Q outputs.
Figure 3.35 gives connection details for the 74LS273 as an
eight bit data latch. The latching pulse should be a negative
type (i.e. the "latch" input is normally high, and it is pulsed

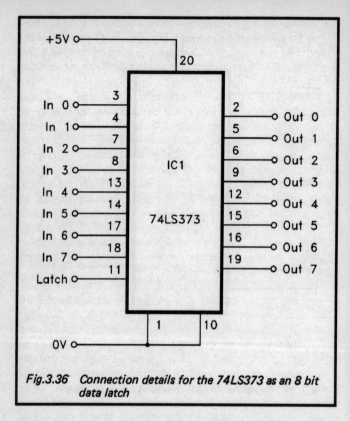

Fig.3.36 Connection details for the 74LS373 as an 8 bit data latch

low to latch a new byte of data). It is on the low to high transition at the end of the pulse that the data is latched. The negative reset input is normally high and must be pulsed low in order to reset all the outputs to the low state. If the reset facility is not required pin 1 should be connected to the +5 volt supply rail.

The 74LS373 octal transparent latch is also useful in data latch applications. Figure 3.36 provides connection details for this device. With the "latch" input high the outputs simply follow the logic states on the inputs. Taking the "latch" input low latches the current data onto the outputs. Therefore, "latch" is normally held low and is pulsed high by the address decoder or other decoder circuit. It is on the high to low transition that the data is latched. Note that this is the opposite to the method of latching provided by the 74LS273. Note also that there is no reset facility available when using the 74LS373.

A computer input port requires a circuit that will only output data onto the bidirectional bus when a pulse is received from the address decoder circuit. With various devices placing data onto the data bus it is obviously imperative that no more than one device at a time tries to drive the bus. This is achieved by only having the bus driven via tristate buffers. The third logic state is an "off" type where the output goes to a high impedance state, so that it has no significant affect on the bus. It is then up to the control logic circuits to ensure that only one device is active at any one time. Of course, multiple outputs driving a common bus is not something that is unique to microprocessor circuits, and this type of thing occurs in many digital applications.

The standard eight bit tristate buffer is the 74LS244. Connection details for this device are provided in Figure 3.37. The "enable" input is a negative type, and it is therefore pulsed low in order to momentarily activate the outputs. In practice this device can be a bit awkward to use since its input and output pins are liberally mixed together, making it necessary to resort to a fairly elaborate printed circuit track pattern. I generally find the 74LS245 octal transceiver to be easier to use in practice, since it conveniently has all the inputs in one row of pins, and all the outputs in the other row. Connection details for the 74LS245 as an 8 bit tristate buffer are shown in Figure 3.38.

It is worth noting that the 74LS373 can also act as a tristate buffer. Pin 11 is tied to the +5 volt supply rail to make the device "transparent", and the control signal is then applied to pin 1. This input is taken high to set the outputs at the third (high impedance) state, or low to produce normal operation.

Analogue-to-Digital and Digital-to-Analogue
For most digital to analogue and analogue to digital converter applications the Ferranti ZN42* and ZN44* series of eight bit

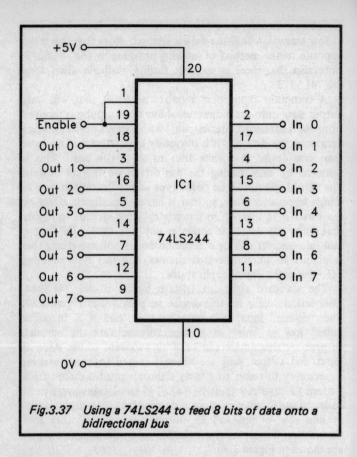

Fig.3.37 *Using a 74LS244 to feed 8 bits of data onto a bidirectional bus*

chips are a good choice. They offer good performance, low cost, and ease of use.

Figure 3.39 shows the circuit diagram for a digital to analogue converter based on the ZN425E. Like all the Ferranti converter chips featured here, it has the sensitivity set by an internal 2.55 volt reference generator. It is possible to use an external reference source, but as the built-in circuit is a very high quality type there is usually no point in doing so. However, pin 15 is the reference input, and pin 16 is the output of the built-in reference source. C1 provides decoupling

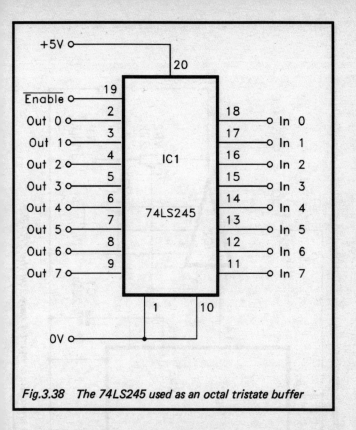

Fig.3.38 The 74LS245 used as an octal tristate buffer

for the reference generator. The eight bit input signal is applied on inputs D0 to D7, and these are TTL compatible.

The output at pin 14 is 2.55 volts full scale (i.e. equal to the reference voltage), which equates to 10 millivolts (0.01 volts) per l.s.b. The output is from an impedance of a few kilohms, and in practice it is normally necessary for the output to be buffered. IC2 acts as the buffer amplifier, and this can also provide voltage amplification so that higher full scale output voltages can be accommodated. VR1 is the offset null control, and this is adjusted for good accuracy at low output voltages. VR2 is the gain control, and this is set to give the required full scale output voltage. Note that the

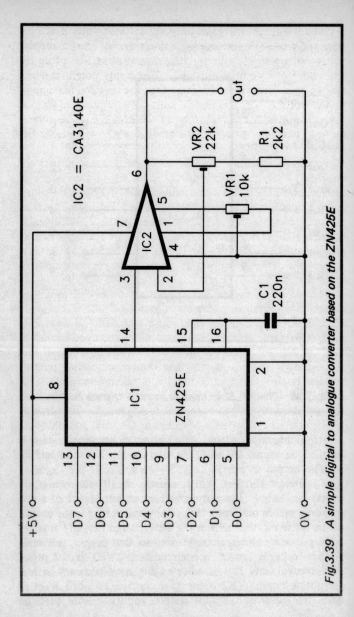

Fig.3.39 A simple digital to analogue converter based on the ZN425E

134

maximum output voltage is only about three volts if IC2 is powered from a 5 volt supply. However, by using a supply voltage of up to 30 volts for IC2, output potentials of up to around 28 volts can be provided. The supply potential must always be at least two volts more than the required maximum output voltage. Of course, IC1 must only be powered from a 5 volt supply. The settling time of the ZN425E is one microsecond, but in a practical circuit this might effectively be reduced slightly by the output amplifier.

Figure 3.40 shows the circuit diagram for a digital to analogue converter based on the ZN426E. This offers a similar level of performance to the circuit of Figure 3.39, but it has a significantly lower current consumption. The ZN425E typically consumes 30 milliamps, whereas the ZN426E only consumes about 5 milliamps. R1 and C1 are the load resistor and decoupling capacitor for the integral 2.55 volt reference source, which has its output at pin 6. The reference input is at pin 5.

The circuit of Figure 3.41 is based on a ZN428E which is compatible with most computer buses. The ZN428E is basically a ZN426E having an eight bit transparent latch at the input. With the "latch" input low the device operates much like the ZN426E. Taking the "latch" input high latches the current data into the device, and the corresponding output voltage is then held until "latch" is taken low again. In normal use "latch" is held high, and is pulsed low by the address decoder or other control logic circuit. The data is latched on the trailing edge of this pulse (i.e. as it goes through a low to high transition). The current consumption of the ZN428E is about 20 milliamps, and its settling time is 800 nanoseconds.

These digital to analogue converter circuits all require an operational amplifier which can operate with its output right down to the 0 volt supply rail. They will work properly with other operational amplifiers if a dual balanced supply is used. In fact it is not necessary to have a balanced supply, as we are not interested in producing negative output voltages. A negative supply of about 3 to 5 volts is adequate, as this will enable any normal operational amplifier to provide an output of 0 volts. An advantage of using a low negative supply potential is that it

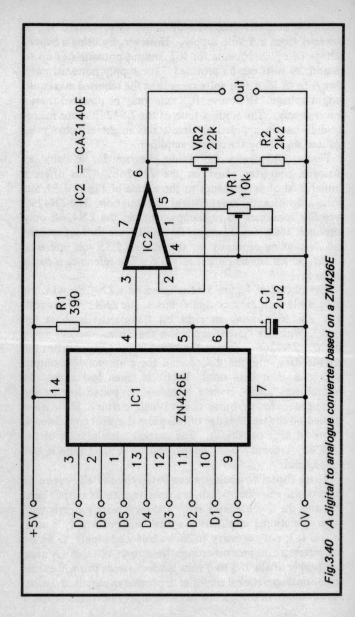

Fig.3.40 A digital to analogue converter based on a ZN426E

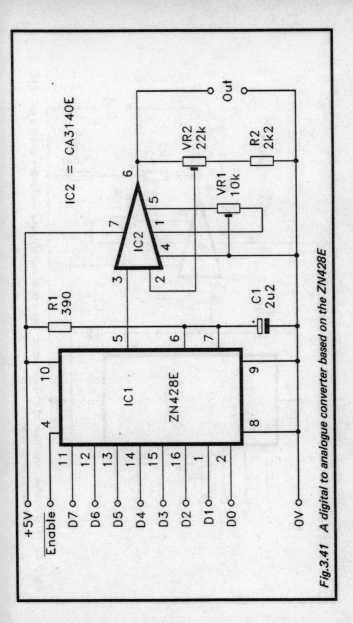

Fig.3.41 A digital to analogue converter based on the ZN428E

137

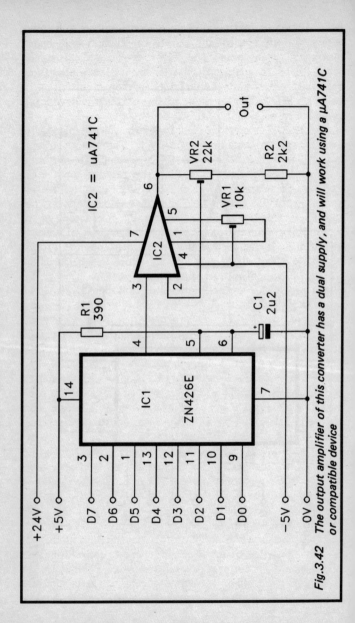

Fig.3.42 The output amplifier of this converter has a dual supply, and will work using a µA741C or compatible device

138

permits a higher maximum positive supply voltage to be used, which in turn enables the circuit to accommodate higher maximum output potentials. Figure 3.42 shows the circuit for a digital to analogue converter which has a dual (non-balanced) supply output amplifier. Although this circuit is based on a ZN426E, this basic scheme of things will work just as well using a ZN425E or ZN428E.

Figure 3.43 shows the circuit diagram for an analogue to digital converter based on a ZN427E. This has an internal 2.55 volt reference voltage source which requires load resistor R1 and decoupling capacitor C1. This sets the input sensitivity of the converter chip at 2.55 volts full scale, but the sensitivity of the circuit as a whole has to be somewhat less than this. This is due to the need for an offset circuit at the input of the unit to compensate for a slight lack of linearity at low input levels. Basically all this circuit does is to provide a positive offset at the input of IC1 which is equal to about 0.5 l.s.b. (or 5 millivolts in other words).

R4 and R5 are an input attenuator, and these give an input sensitivity of about 5.1 volts full scale. Obviously the values used here can be altered to produce other input sensitivities, but the output impedance of this circuit (i.e. the parallel resistance of R4 and R5) should be roughly equal to 4k. Otherwise the offset circuit will not function properly. VR1 and R3 provide the offset voltage. To give VR1 the correct setting the circuit should be fed with an input voltage equal to 0.5 l.s.b. (which is 10 millivolts with a full scale sensitivity of 5.1 volts). VR1 is then adjusted to give returned readings that alternate between 0 and 1.

R2 is the "tail" resistor for the voltage comparator at the input of the converter. This must be fed from a negative supply, but the current flow through R2 is only about 50 microamps or so. R2 should be 47k for a -3 volt supply, or 180k for a -12 volt supply.

The digital inputs and outputs of IC1 are all TTL compatible. An external clock generator is required, and this can have a frequency of up to 600kHz. Each conversion takes about nine clock cycles incidentally. To start a conversion pin 4 must be pulsed low. A hold-off of at least nine clock cycles in duration must then be provided before a reading is taken.

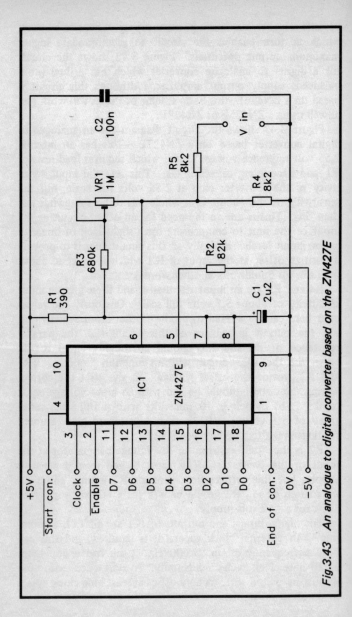

Fig.3.43 An analogue to digital converter based on the ZN427E

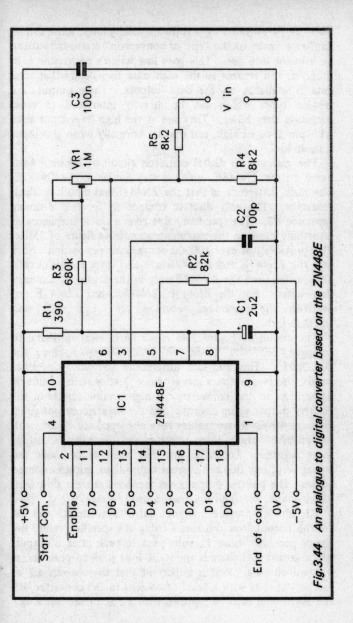

Fig.3.44 An analogue to digital converter based on the ZN448E

141

This can be provided by a software timing loop, some sort of hardware timer, or the "end of conversion" status output can be brought into use. This goes low while a conversion is in progress, and returns to the high state to indicate that valid data is available on the data outputs. These outputs are tristate types which can be directly interfaced to most computer data buses. They are at the high impedance state with pin 2 taken high, and operate normally when this input is taken low.

The analogue to digital converter circuit of Figure 3.44 is based on the ZN448E, which is very similar to the ZN427E. The main difference is that the ZN448E has a built-in clock generator. The only discrete component for this is timing capacitor C2. The specified value gives a clock frequency of something close to the maximum acceptable figure of 1MHz. This provides just over 100000 conversions per second. Note that the ZN447E and ZN449E will also work in this circuit. They differ from the ZN448E only in the degree of accuracy they offer. For the ZN449E, ZN448E, and ZN447E respectively, the guaranteed accuracies are 1 l.s.b., 0.5 l.s.b., and 0.25 l.s.b.

The circuit of Figure 3.45 is for an interesting digital to analogue converter based on a non-Ferranti chip, the DAC0801. This provides differential outputs. In other words, the two outputs are at about 0 volts with a value of 64 written to the converter. A higher value results in the positive output going negative, and the negative output going more positive. Lower values have the opposite effect, with the positive output going positive, and the negative output going negative. Logically, this may seem to be round the wrong way, but this is a current rather than voltage oriented device. The positive output gives increased current flow with higher values, which gives a lower output voltage.

R1 and R2 provide reference currents, while R3 and R4 are the output load resistors. Using the specified values the circuit provides about 12 volts peak to peak at each output, which means that there is about 24 volts peak to peak across the two outputs. If it is important that the outputs are at precisely 0 volts with a value of 64 sent to the converter, R3 and R4 should each be replaced with a 10k preset and a 4k7

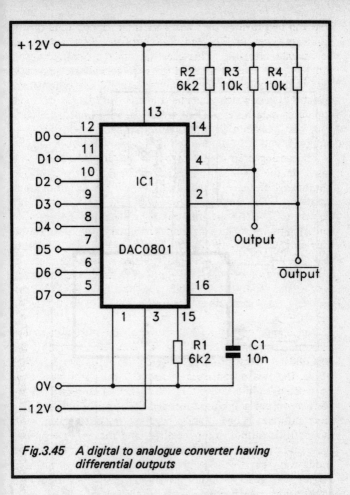

Fig.3.45 A digital to analogue converter having differential outputs

fixed resistor connected in series. The presets can then be adjusted to trim the outputs to precisely 0 volts.

Stepper Driver

The circuit of Figure 3.46 is for a four phase stepper motor driver. The stepper motor should not draw an output current of more than 500 milliamps, and it must be connected to the

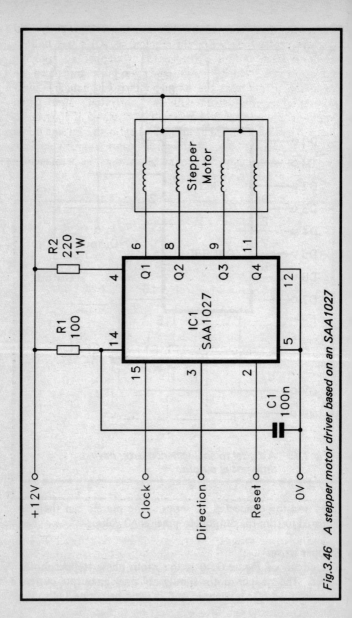

Fig.3.46   A stepper motor driver based on an SAA1027

driver circuit correctly if the system is to work properly. No discrete protection diodes are required as IC1 has a built-in diode at each output. The motor is stepper by applying pulses to the "clock" input, and the pulse rate must be restricted to one that the stepper motor can handle. Clockwise rotation is obtained with the "direction" input taken low — counter clockwise rotation is obtained if it is taken high. The "reset" input is normally held high. Pulsing it low takes the outputs back to their initial states. In many applications this input is not needed, and it can then be permanently wired to the positive supply rail.

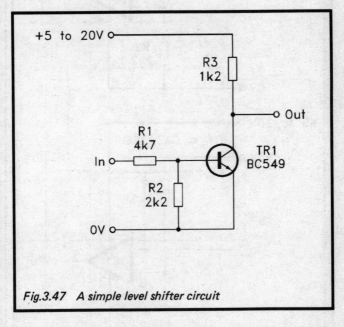

Fig.3.47   A simple level shifter circuit

It is important to note that this stepper motor driver requires control signals at 12 volt levels, not 5 volt TTL or CMOS logic levels. If the circuit is to be driven from 5 volt logic circuits some simple level shifting will be needed at each input. Figure 3.47 shows the circuit diagram for a simple level shifter that can be used with the stepper motor driver circuit,

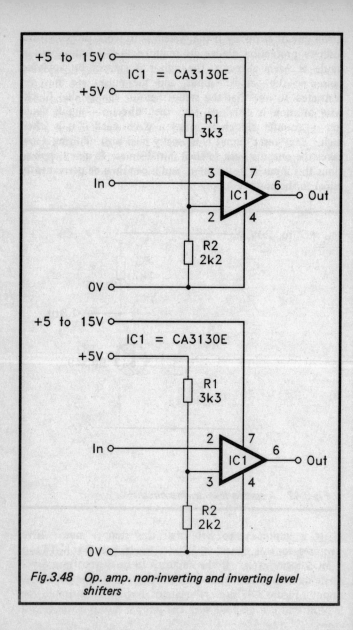

Fig.3.48 Op. amp. non-inverting and inverting level
shifters

146

or with any circuit that requires a similar change in voltage levels. Of course, for operation with the stepper motor driver a 12 volt supply should be used. Bear in mind that this circuit provides an inversion between the input and the output.

The circuits of Figure 3.48 are for two simple operational amplifier level shifter circuits. The upper circuit is non-inverting, while the lower circuit provides an inversion. The circuit of Figure 3.49 is basically the same as that of Figure 3.47, but it is designed to level shift in the opposite direction (i.e. 6 to 18 volt logic input levels are converted to 5 volt logic output levels).

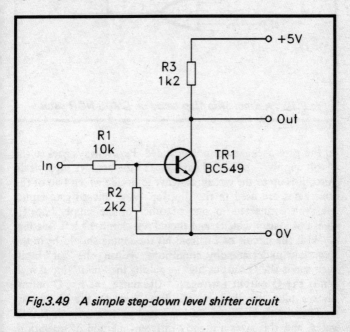

Fig.3.49   A simple step-down level shifter circuit

Simple Flip/Flops

Simple but very useful flip/flop circuits can be produced from CMOS NAND and NOR gates. Figure 3.50 shows the method of connection needed to produce a flip/flop from two 2 input NOR gates. Note that for the sake of simplicity in all the flip/flop circuits shown here, the supply connections

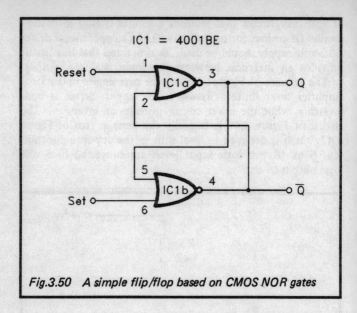

IC1 = 4001BE

Reset o—

IC1a

Set o—

IC1b

Q

Q̄

Fig.3.50   A simple flip/flop based on CMOS NOR gates

to the gate package are not included. Pin 7 always goes to the
0 volt supply — pin 14 always goes to the positive supply rail.
Also, it is up to the circuit designer to decide which two of the
four gates are used in the flip/flop. Any unused gate inputs
must be connected to one or other of the supply lines (it
does not matter which), and should not simply be left floating.

With the circuit of Figure 3.50 the inputs should be in the
low state under standby conditions. Pulsing the "set" input
high sends the Q output high — pulsing the "reset" input high
sends the Q output low again. Of course, the not Q output
always takes up the opposite logic level to the Q output.

The circuit of Figure 3.51 is based on two 2 input NAND
gates, and this gives a slightly different method of operation.
Under standby conditions the inputs should be held high,
and they are pulsed low in order to set and reset the flip/flop.
Note that with both circuits predictable operation is only
obtained if one input at a time is activated. A useful property
of these circuits is that they consume no significant power
under standby conditions.

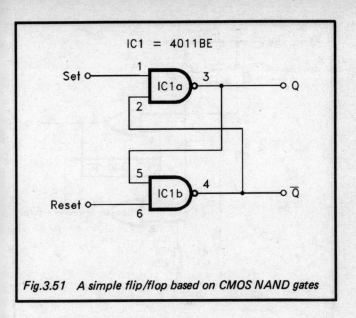

Fig.3.51   A simple flip/flop based on CMOS NAND gates

In practical applications it is often necessary to have manual control of a flip/flop. Figures 3.52 and 3.53 show how the two basic flip/flop circuits can be operated via push-button switches. In the circuit of Figure 3.54 the flip/flop is controlled via touch contacts. Although there is no obvious way in which the input signals to the flip/flop are obtained, this type of circuit works well in practice. Due to the high value of the input resistors, electrical noise picked up in the operator's body and fed to the inputs via the touch contacts will operate the flip/flop reliably. The same method of control will work with a NAND gate flip/flop, but R1 and R2 must then connect the inputs of the flip/flop to the positive supply rail.

Figure 3.55 shows another approach to touch control, and this circuit is based on a simple CMOS latch circuit. Although it is shown as being based on three NAND gates, these are all wired to act as simple inverters. Hence this circuit (and the next two circuits) will actually work using any CMOS inverters or gates connected to operate as inverters.

149

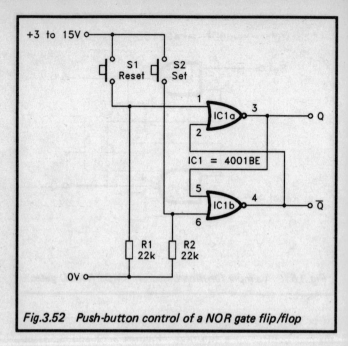

Fig.3.52   Push-button control of a NOR gate flip/flop

This circuit relies on skin resistance rather than stray pickup of electrical noise. In fact C1 is needed to filter out noise which might otherwise cause erratic operation of the circuit. Touching the upper two contacts pulls the input of the circuit and the Q output high — touching the lower pair of contacts pulls the input and the Q output low again.

The circuit of Figure 3.56 offers another, and more novel approach to touch control. This circuit again relies on skin resistance, but it provides successive operation. In other words, touching the contacts sets the Q output high, touching the contacts again sets it low, touching the contacts a third time sets the Q output high again, and so on. Figure 3.57 provides the circuit for a push-button version of Figure 3.56.

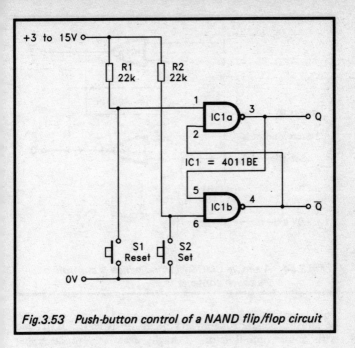

Fig.3.53 Push-button control of a NAND flip/flop circuit

Opto-Isolators

Opto-isolators provide a simple means of coupling logic
signals from one circuit to another while providing complete
electrical isolation between the two circuits. Most opto-
isolators can withstand voltage spikes of up to at least 2500
volts between the input and output circuits. The most
important point to bear in mind with normal opto-isolators
is that they are very slow in comparison to logic circuits.

Figure 3.58 shows a simple opto-isolator circuit that will
couple logic levels from the input to the output, and this
will work using virtually any "bog standard" otpo-isolator.
At best it will only couple squarewave signals of up to a few
kilohertz. It will not reliably handle pulses of much under
one millisecond in duration.

The circuit of Figure 3.59 gives more reliable operation,
and can handle higher frequencies. This arrangement should

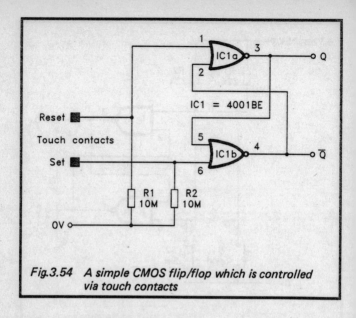

Fig.3.54 A simple CMOS flip/flop which is controlled via touch contacts

be able to handle squarewaves of up to at least 50kHz, and with some opto-isolators it might even achieve an upper frequency limit of around ten times this figure. This is still rather low by logic circuit standards, but it is sufficient for many applications. The circuit of Figure 3.60 achieves a similar level of performance by using a high quality opto-isolator which includes a built-in transistor amplifier at the output.

Electronic music equipment which is fitted with a MIDI interface must have an opto-isolator at the MIDI input. Figure 3.61 shows the circuit diagram for an opto-isolated MIDI input stage. The MIDI baud rate is 31250, which is high enough to necessitate the use of a high quality opto-islator. The circuit includes a MIDI THRU output (omit R4 and R5 if this facility is not required).

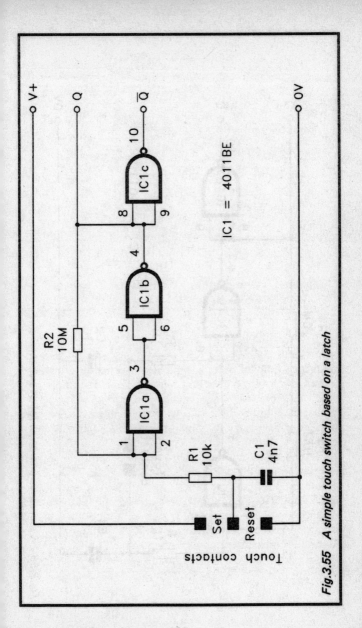

Fig.3.55 A simple touch switch based on a latch

153

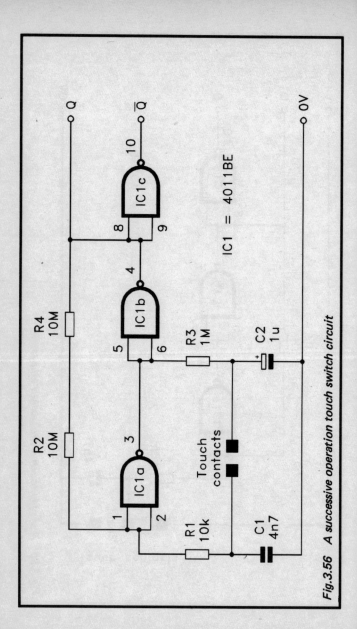

Fig.3.56 A successive operation touch switch circuit

154

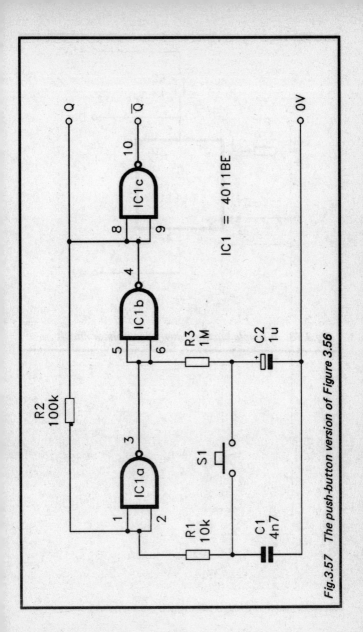

Fig.3.57 The push-button version of Figure 3.56

IC1 = 4011BE

155

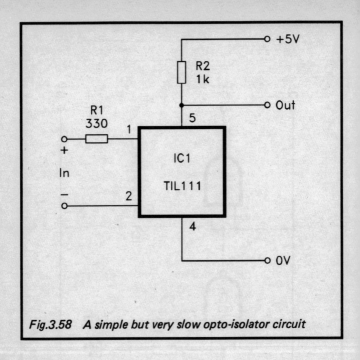

Fig.3.58   A simple but very slow opto-isolator circuit

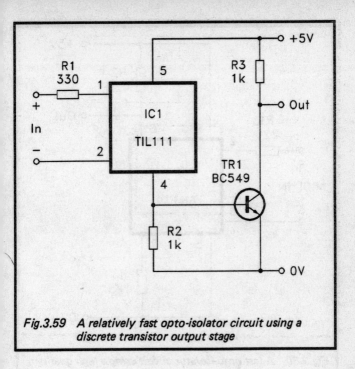

Fig.3.59 A relatively fast opto-isolator circuit using a discrete transistor output stage

157

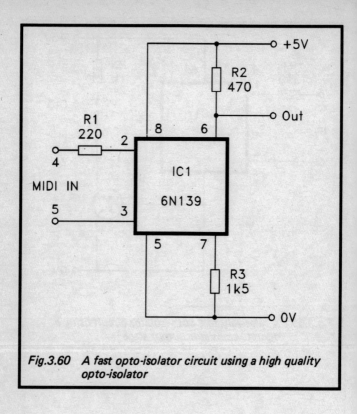

Fig.3.60   A fast opto-isolator circuit using a high quality opto-isolator

158

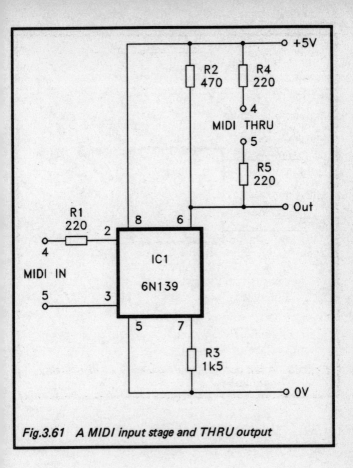

Fig.3.61   A MIDI input stage and THRU output

Chapter 4

POWER SUPPLIES, ETC.

The circuit diagram of Figure 4.1 is for a basic full-wave power supply circuit using push-pull rectification. The unloaded d.c. output voltage is approximately 1.5 times the a.c. voltage rating of T1, or about 18 volts in this example which uses a 12 volt transformer. Under full load the output voltage drops substantially. In fact it drops to something not too far removed from the voltage rating of the mains transformer. This large variation in output voltage makes non-stabilised supplies unsuitable for many applications. The current rating of T1 should be equal to or slightly higher than the required maximum d.c. output current.

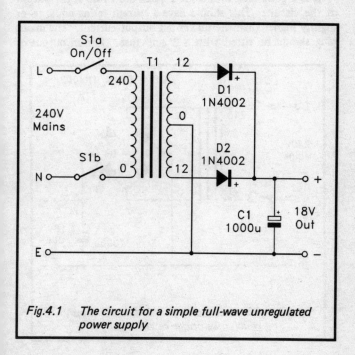

Fig.4.1   The circuit for a simple full-wave unregulated power supply

The voltage rating of D1 and D2 should be at least double the unloaded d.c. output voltage. The 1N4002 has a p.i.v. rating of 100 volts, which makes it suitable for unloaded output voltages of up to 50 volts (use 1N4003s for unloaded output voltages of up to 100 volts). The 1N400* series of rectifiers can handle output currents of up to 1 amp. The 1N540* series can be used for higher output currents of up to 3 amps. The correct value for C1 depends on the maximum output current, and the degree of smoothing required. As a general "rule of thumb", at least 1μ per milliamp of output current is needed to provide good results. Obviously the voltage rating of C1 should be comfortably more than the unloaded output voltage. I generally choose a voltage rating which is about double the loaded d.c. output voltage, and for the example 12 volt power supply a rating of 25 volts would therefore be suitable.

It is a good idea to include a quick-blow fuse at the output of the circuit. This should have a current rating equal to or slightly higher than the maximum output current. The mains plug should be fitted with a 2 amp fuse. For an output of

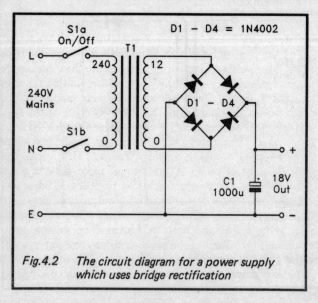

Fig.4.2   The circuit diagram for a power supply
which uses bridge rectification

the opposite polarity (i.e. a positive earth supply) simply reverse the polarities of D1, D2, and C1.

Figure 4.2 shows the circuit diagram for a basic mains power supply which uses full-wave bridge rectification. Most of the notes about the push-pull power supply circuit also apply to this one. However, there is an important difference in that the current rating of the mains transformer should be about 1.5 times the maximum output current. For a positive earth supply reverse the polarities of C1 and the four rectifiers.

For dual balanced supplies the circuit of Figure 4.3 can be used. This is basically just two push-pull type rectifier circuits driven from a common mains transformer. One rectifier provides the positive supply, the other produces the negative supply. The current rating of the mains transformer should be about 1.5 times the maximum d.c. output current.

It has to be pointed out that circuits which involve connections to the mains supply are potentially lethal, and should only be undertaken by those who have sufficient experience of electronic circuit building. Beginners should restrict themselves to battery powered circuits until they have gained the necessary experience.

Regulators

A stabilised power supply is basically just a non-regulated type feeding into a voltage regulator circuit. In use the most simple voltage regulators are the three terminal monolithic types in the μA78** series. These are available with various output voltage ratings, as indicated by the last two digits of the type number (e.g. the μA7805 is a 5 volt type, and the μA7812 is a 12 volt type). The basic μA78** series can handle maximum output currents of up to 1 amp. The μA78L** series can handle currents of up to 100 milliamps, the μA78M** series are suitable for output currents of up to 500 milliamps, and the μA78S** devices can operate with output currents of up to 2 amps. All except the μA78L** series will become quite hot in normal use, and must be mounted on suitable heatsinks. All these devices are protected by output current limiting of the "foldback" variety.

The only discrete components required are two decoupling capacitors, as can be seen from the circuit of Figure 4.4.

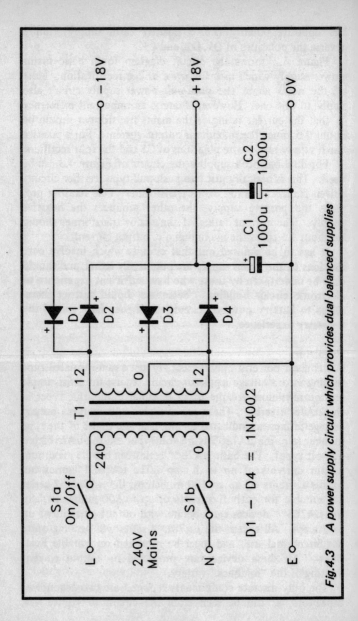

Fig.4.3   A power supply circuit which provides dual balanced supplies

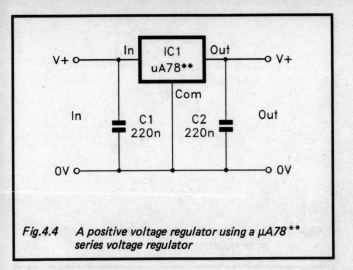

Fig.4.4 *A positive voltage regulator using a μA78** series voltage regulator*

These capacitors should be fitted close to IC1. A well smoothed and regulated output will be produced, but only if the input voltage is always about three volts or more higher than the output voltage. The maximum permissible input voltage rating varies somewhat from one device to another, but is generally about 35 volts. However, it is advisable not to have high voltage drops across the regulator, as this could result in it producing large amounts of heat.

If a negative supply is required, it is just a matter of using a μA79** series regulator in place of the μA78** type, as shown in the circuit of Figure 4.5. The notes about Figure 4.4 apply equally to Figure 4.5.

One slight problem with the three terminal monolithic voltage regulators is that only a small range of output voltages are available. The situation can be improved slightly using a boosted regulator circuit, such as the one shown in Figure 4.6. R1, D1, and D2 form a simple voltage regulator circuit which takes the "com" terminal of IC1 about 1.2 volts above the 0 volt supply potential. The regulator works much as before, but the output voltage is increased by about 1.2 volts. Using a 5 volt regulator in this configuration would therefore give an output potential of just over 6 volts. Use a

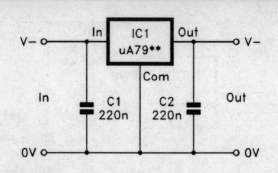

Fig.4.5   A negative voltage regulator using a μA79**
series regulator chip

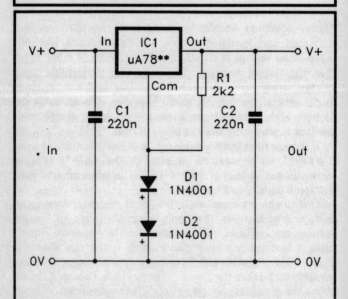

Fig.4.6   A simple "boosted" regulator configuration

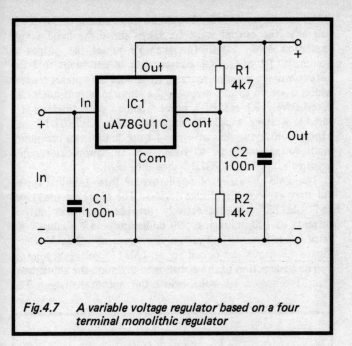

*Fig.4.7   A variable voltage regulator based on a four
terminal monolithic regulator*

single rectifier for a boost of 0.6 volts, or three in series for
a boost of about 1.8 volts. Note that using any boosted
regulator configuration is likely to give a slight loss of
performance from the regulator.

Figure 4.7 shows the circuit diagram for a voltage
stabiliser based on a four terminal regulator chip (the
μA78GU1C). This chip can provide an output voltage of
anything from 5 to 30 volts, and the output voltage is
controlled by the values of R1 and R2. The output voltage
can be calculated from this formula:-

$$V out = [(R1 + R2)/(R2)] \times 5 \text{ volts}$$

The basic action of the circuit is to stabilise the control
("cont") input at 5 volts by negative feedback. This
stabilises the output voltage at a higher level which is deter-
mined by the voltage drop produced by R1 and R2. With

R2 at a value of 4k7, R1 should be given a value of 940R per volt that the output must be taken above the basic 5 volt regulation level. With the example values the output is nominally 10 volts. Of course, if it is important that the output voltage is very accurate, R1 should be a preset resistor which is set up to give precisely the required output potential. Alternatively R1 can be a panel mounted potentiometer if a variable voltage supply is required. The μA78GU1C can handle output currents of up to 1 amp, and it has a maximum input voltage rating of 40 volts. For an equivalent variable negative supply a μA79GU1C should be used.

The LM317* series of regulators are three terminal types, but they are variable voltage devices. The LM317L, LM317M, and LM317T can respectively provide maximum output currents of 100 milliamps, 500 milliamps, and 1.5 amps. All three types have an output voltage range of 1.2 to 37 volts. Figure 4.8 shows the circuit for an LM317* voltage regulator.

The basic action of the circuit is to maintain the adjustment ("adj") terminal 1.2 volts below the output voltage. The

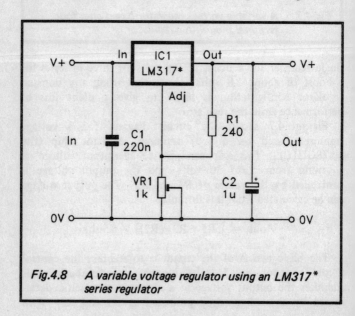

Fig.4.8 *A variable voltage regulator using an LM317* series regulator*

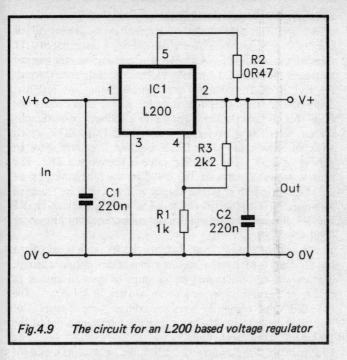

Fig.4.9   The circuit for an L200 based voltage regulator

current which flows through R1 and VR1 generates a voltage across VR1, and the output is therefore regulated at this voltage plus 1.2 volts. To determine the correct value for VR1 for a given output voltage, first deduct 1.2 from the required output voltage, and then multiply by 200. This gives the value for VR1 in ohms. Using the example 1k preset for VR1 the output is adjustable from about 1.2 to 6.2 volts. The maximum permissible input to output voltage for the LM317* series is 40 volts. The LM317* devices all have output current limiting, but this is not of the "foldback" variety.

The L200 is one of the most advanced regulator chips currently available. It enables both the output voltage and maximum output current to be varied. The output voltage can be anything from 2.85 to 36 volts, and the input voltage range is 4.85 to 40 volts. Output currents of up to 2 amps can be accommodated. Figure 4.9 shows the circuit diagram for a voltage regulator based on this chip.

R1 and R3 control the output voltage. The circuit is stabilised by negative feedback which gives a potential of 2.77 volts at pin 4 of IC1. With R1 at a value of 1k, the output voltage is therefore 2.77 volts per kilohm of resistance through R1 and R3. To calculate the required value for R3, first divide the required output voltage by 2.77. Then deduct one from this to give the value for R3 in kilohms. For example, for an output of 12 volts we first divided 12 by 2.77, which gives an answer of 4.33. Deducting one from this gives an answer of 3.33. The required value is therefore 3.33k. The nearest preferred value of 3k3 could be used, or a 4k7 preset could be fitted so that the output voltage could be trimmed to precisely the required figure. The specified values for R1 and R3, incidentally, provide an output potential of just under 9 volts.

R2 sets the output limit current, and its value is calculated by dividing 0.45 by the required maximum output current. The output current should be in amps to give an answer in ohms, or in milliamps to give an answer in kilohms. The specified value obviously gives a maximum output current of just under one amp. The output current limiting is not of the "foldback" type incidentally.

Figure 4.10 shows how the L200 can be used as a current regulator. Pin 4 is simply tied to the 0 volt supply rail so that the output is forced to the maximum possible output voltage. The output current limiting circuit then provides control of the output voltage, so as to set the required output current flow. Obviously the circuit can only work properly if the load across the output provides a low enough resistance to permit the required current to flow.

If high performance is not required and only low output currents are involved, a simple zener shunt stabiliser of the type shown in Figure 4.11 should suffice. The value of R1 is calculated to give a current flow of 5 milliamps, plus the required output current (which should be less than 5 milliamps). Suppose that the nominal input voltage is 15 volts, the required output voltage is 9 volts, and that an output current of one milliamp is required. There are no 9 volt zeners, but the nearest preferred value of 9.1 volts is close

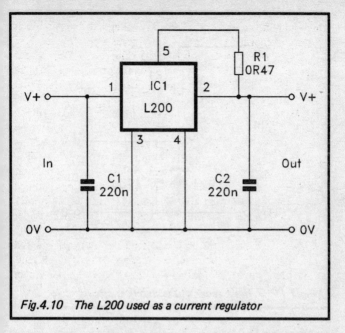

Fig.4.10 The L200 used as a current regulator

enough. This gives six volts across R1, and we require a current flow here of 6 milliamps. Applying Ohm's Law, this clearly gives an answer of 1k (6 volts divided by 0.006 amps = 1000 ohms or 1k). Note that most zener diodes have a tolerance of 5% on their voltage ratings. Zeners having operating voltages of about 6.8 volts or more are generally more efficient than those having operating voltages of less than 6.8 volts.

For non-critical applications which require output currents of up to about 50 milliamps, a simple series regulator of the type shown in Figure 4.12 should be suitable. The zener (D1) should have an operating voltage about 0.5 to one volt higher than the required output potential in order to compensate for the voltage drop through emitter follower TR1. This circuit can handle input voltages of up to about 20 volts or so. Using a BC337 for TR1 enables input potentials of up to about 45 volts to be accommodated. The value of R1 is chosen to give a current flow of about 5 milliamps.

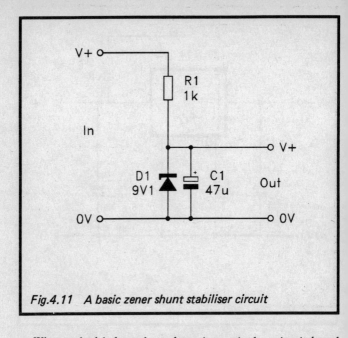

Fig.4.11   A basic zener shunt stabiliser circuit

When a dual balanced regulator is required, a circuit based on µA78** and µA79** regulators is usually the simplest means of obtaining the desired result (Fig.4.13). If dual 15 volt supplies for an operational amplifier circuit are required, the 4195 dual regulator is a popular choice. The basic 4195 dual balanced regulator circuit appears in Figure 4.14. This can provide up to 100 milliamps per output, but in practice the maximum dissipation figure for the 4195 might restrict the maximum output current to slightly less than this. The dissipation should not exceed 600 milliwatts.

The output voltages of this circuit can be out of balance by as much as 1 volt, although the accuracy would typically be much better than this. In most applications a substantial mismatch of the output voltages will not be of any practical importance. However, the circuit of Figure 4.15 can be used if highly accurate matching is needed. Adjustment of VR1 permits the output voltages to be precisely balanced.

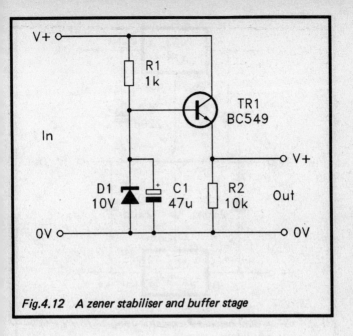

Fig.4.12   A zener stabiliser and buffer stage

Splitters, Etc.

In some dual supply applications a sort of pseudo dual balanced supply will suffice. The basic idea is to have (say) a 30 volt supply with a supply splitter which provides a sort of centre tap on the supply. This centre tap effectively becomes the central 0 volt rail, the two input supplies being +15 volts and −15 volts relative to this. The circuit of Figure 4.16 is for a low power splitter which can provide output currents of no more than a few milliamps. The circuit of Figure 4.17 can accommodate output currents of up to one amp provided IC1 is mounted on a substantial heatsink. Both circuits consist of a potential divider feeding into an operational amplifier voltage follower circuit. The circuit of Figure 4.16 will work well with input voltages in the range 9 to 30 volts. The input voltage range for the circuit of Figure 4.17 is 12 to 30 volts. With both circuits R1 and R2 should be 1% tolerance components if good accuracy is required.

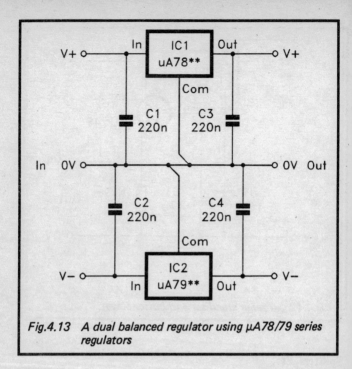

Fig.4.13 A dual balanced regulator using μA78/79 series regulators

Some applications require a positive supply which might have to handle output currents of an amp or more, plus a negative supply which will supply no more than a few milliamps. A dual balanced supply clearly provides a lot of "overkill" in such a situation. Generating the low power negative supply from the positive supply offers what is often a more practical approach to the problem. Figure 4.18 shows the circuit for a simple negative supply generator based on an ICL7660. Note that there is a fair amount of noise on the −5 volt output. Also, this output "sags" significantly under loading, and it has a source resistance of about 70 ohms. Obviously this type of circuit is unsuitable for critical applications. The maximum output current should not exceed 40 milliamps.

The circuit of Figure 4.19 shows a simple and inexpensive method of generating a −3 volt output from a +5 volt supply.

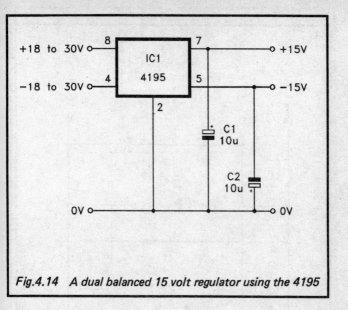

Fig.4.14   A dual balanced 15 volt regulator using the 4195

This circuit is not very efficient, and can only supply currents of about one milliamp or less. However, it is useful for producing the negative supply for a ZN427E or ZN448E analogue to digital converter, or any similar low current application.

The circuit of Figure 4.20 uses a 555 oscillator in a similar manner to generate a negative output that is about 1.5 volts less than the positive supply potential. This circuit will provide output currents of 30 milliamps or more, but the higher the output current that is drawn, the lower the output voltage will be pulled. With low input voltages it may therefore be impractical to draw output currents of more than a few milliamps. In the circuit of Figure 4.21 much the same technique is used, but a positive output voltage is generated, and this is added to the positive supply potential. This gives a so-called voltage doubler effect. In reality the output voltage will not be doubled, due to the voltage drop through the rectifiers and the fact that IC1 will provide a peak to peak output voltage of something less than the full supply voltage.

175

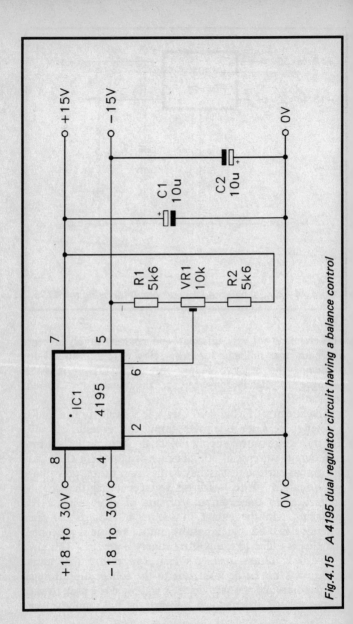

Fig.4.15 A 4195 dual regulator circuit having a balance control

176

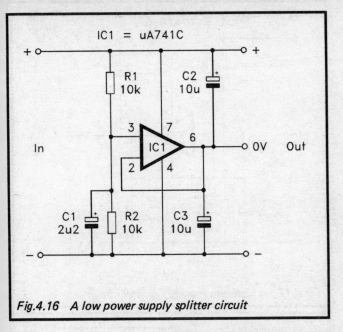

Fig.4.16 A low power supply splitter circuit

With a 5 volt supply the voltage boost is about 50 to 60%. Using a 15 volt supply it is closer to a true doubling action, but the boost will still only be about 80 to 90%.

The circuit of Figure 4.22 uses a voltage doubling rectifier and smoothing circuit to give a negative output voltage that is theoretically double the positive supply voltage. Due to inefficiencies in the components this level of performance is not achieved in practice, and the problem is compounded by the fact that using two rectifier circuits gives double the loading on the output of IC1 for a given output current. Using a 5 volt supply the circuit will provide an output of −5 volts at an output current of a several milliamps. On higher supply voltages something closer to a true voltage doubling action is obtained. The voltage booster circuit of Figure 4.23 uses a voltage doubler which adds to the input supply so as to give a voltage trebling action. In reality this circuit will only give about 10 volts from a 5 volt supply, although it becomes more efficient as the input voltage is increased.

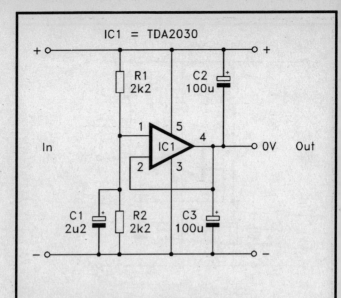

Fig.4.17   A high power supply splitter circuit

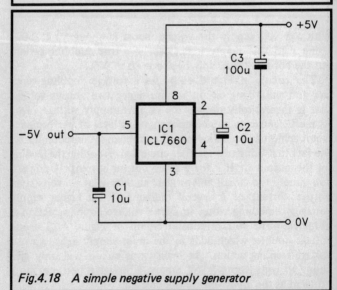

Fig.4.18   A simple negative supply generator

178

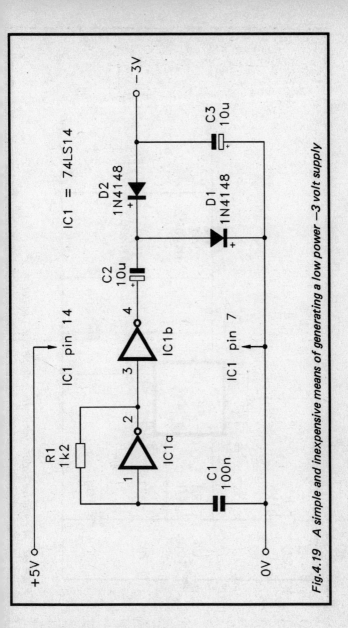

Fig.4.19   A simple and inexpensive means of generating a low power −3 volt supply

179

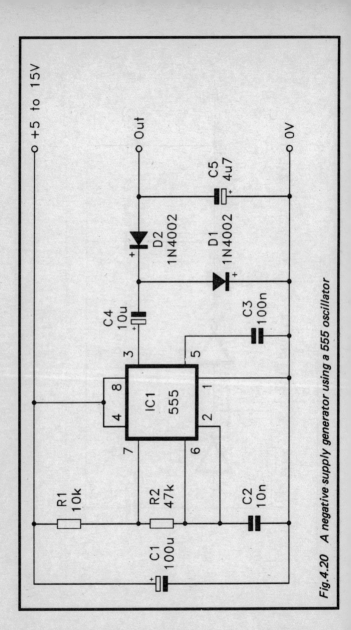

Fig.4.20   A negative supply generator using a 555 oscillator

180

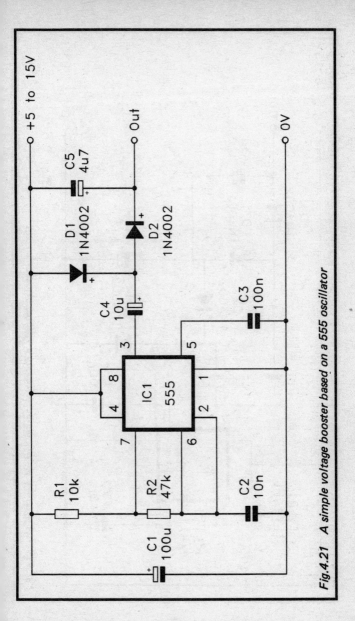

Fig.4.21 A simple voltage booster based on a 555 oscillator

181

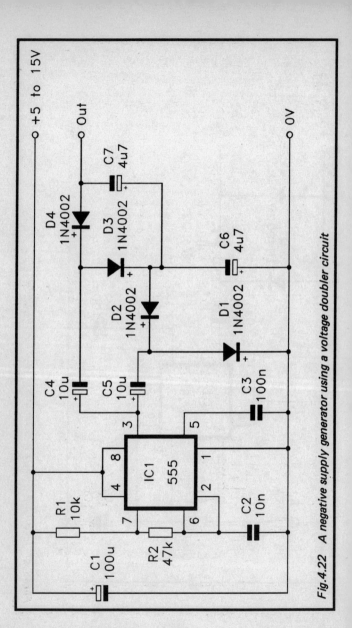

Fig.4.22 A negative supply generator using a voltage doubler circuit

182

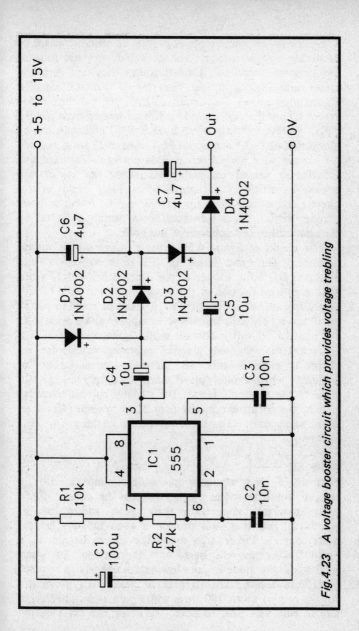

Fig.4.23   A voltage booster circuit which provides voltage trebling

Switch mode power supplies provide an efficient means of producing voltage step-ups, voltage step-downs, and generating negative supplies. Unfortunately, they are generally rather more tricky to use than simple regulator circuits. Figure 4.24 shows the circuit diagram for a switch mode power supply that will provide a voltage step-up from 5 to 12 volts. Output currents of up to about 150 milliamps can be accommodated. L1 consists of 26.5 turns of 22 s.w.g. enamelled copper wire wound on an RM8 potcore. Provided this inductor is wound reasonably accurately the circuit will achieve an efficiency of around 65%. More details of this circuit, and others using the TL497, can be found in book number BP192 "More Advanced Power Supply Projects" by the same author and publisher as this book.

The circuit of Figure 4.25 is for a simple supply voltage monitor. The basic action of IC1 is to switch on l.e.d. indicator D1 if the voltage at pin 3 drops below 1.15 volts. VR1 supplies a fraction of the supply voltage to pin 3 of IC1. Depending on the setting of VR1, D1 can be made to switch on if the supply falls below any threshold voltage from 1.15 volts to the 30 volt maximum supply voltage rating of IC1. In reality the minimum practical operating voltage for the circuit is about 3 volts. R1 provides a small amount of hysteresis which avoids "jitter" when the supply voltage falls close to the threshold level. The standby current consumption of the circuit is typically only 22 microamps (40 microamps maximum). The l.e.d. current is set internally at 7 milliamps.

Noise, Etc.

Normally a zener regulator has a decoupling capacitor to remove the noise spikes generated across the device. For a noise generator application these noise spikes can be amplified, and they will provide a good quality "white" noise source. Figure 4.26 shows the circuit diagram for a "white" noise generator based on a zener diode. The signal level across the diode is quite low, and is unlikely to be much more than a few millivolts peak to peak. IC1 provides a voltage gain of about 180 times which gives an output level of around one volt peak to peak. However, the exact output

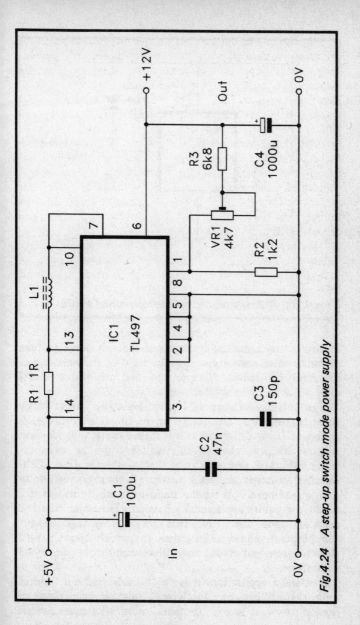

Fig.4.24 A step-up switch mode power supply

185

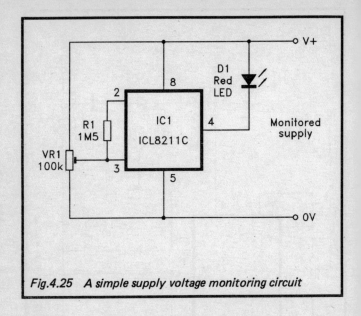

Fig.4.25   A simple supply voltage monitoring circuit

level will vary significantly from one zener diode to another.
A zener noise source can provide noise at frequencies well
into the v.h.f. range. Note though, that this circuit is only
designed as an audio noise source.

The circuit of Figure 4.27 is another audio "white" noise
generator, and it is very similar to the circuit of Figure 4.26.
In fact the only difference is that it uses a reverse biased base-
emitter junction used in this way provides an avalanche
action which is very similar to that of a zener diode. The
effective "zener" voltage is somewhere in the region of 7 volts.
Like a zener circuit, a bipolar transistor used in this way will
produce a significant amount of noise. The noise output is
generally much higher than that from a zener diode though.
The output level from this circuit is typically about 5 volts
peak to peak, but it will vary substantially from one BC549
to another.

For some applications it is "pink" noise and not "white"
noise that is required. In "white" noise all frequencies are
present at equal levels. In "pink" noise all frequencies are

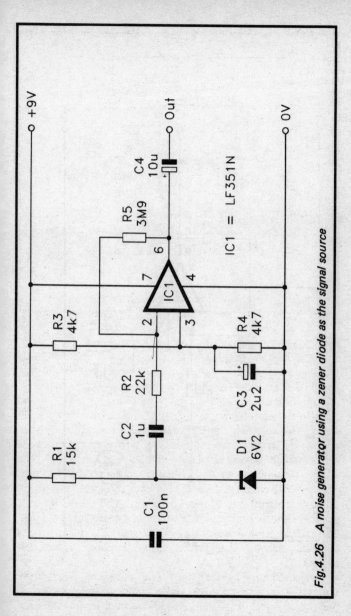

Fig.4.26 A noise generator using a zener diode as the signal source

+9V

Out

0V

C4
10u

R5
3M9

7
6
IC1
4
2
3

IC1 = LF351N

R3
4k7

R4
4k7

R2
22k

C3
2u2

C2
1u

R1
15k

D1
6V2

C1
100n

187

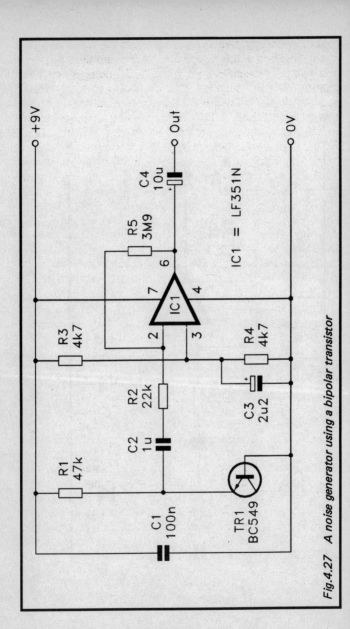

Fig.4.27   A noise generator using a bipolar transistor

188

present, with any two octave bands having identical signal levels. In practice this means that "white" noise gives quite a high pitched "hissing" sound, while "pink" noise gives a lower pitched "shoosh" sound. It is possible to convert "white" noise to "pink" noise using a lowpass filter having a 3dB per octave roll-off rate. This is an awkward attenuation rate which is not easy to produce accurately. The circuit of Figure 4.28 is reasonably simple, but will give quite a good "pink" noise output if it is fed from a "white" noise source.

The circuit of Figure 4.29 is for a simple temperature sensor. It is based on an LM335 which provides an output voltage equal to 10 millivolts (0.01 volts) per kelvin. In ordinary degrees celsius, this works out at 2.73 volts plus 10 millivolts per degree. VR1 is the calibration control, and it is set for an output potential of 2.98 volts with the sensor (IC1) at 25 degrees celsius. The LM335Z covers a temperature range of −10 degrees celsius to 100 degrees celsius with excellent linearity.

Figure 4.30 shows the circuit diagrams for two temperature sensors based on the LM35DZ. These provide an output of 10 millivolts per degree celsius, and do not require any calibration. The circuit on the left requires only a single supply rail and no discrete components. It covers a temperature range of 2 to 100 degrees celsius. The circuit on the right requires a negative supply and one discrete component. It covers a temperature range of 0 to 100 degrees celsius. The quiescent current consumption is typically 56 microamps, which ensures minimal self-heating of the sensor chip.

The circuit of Figure 4.31 is for a phase locked loop (p.l.l.) tone decoder. If a tone within the lock-on range is applied to the input, the open collector output transistor is switched on and pin 8 is pulled low. The output can sink up to 100 milliamps, and it is logic compatible if the circuit is powered from a 5 volt supply. R2 and C5 are the timing components which set the centre frequency. The centre frequency is given by the formula:-

$$\text{Frequency} = 1.1/(\text{R2 C5})$$

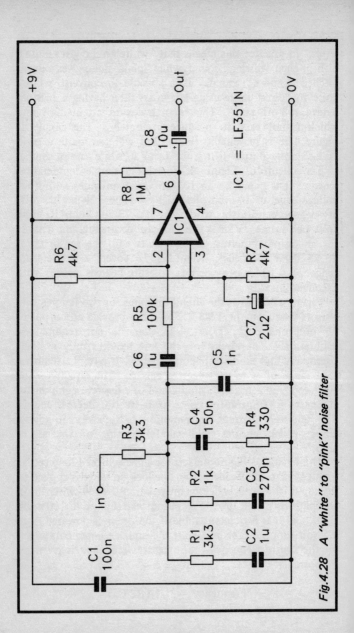

Fig.4.28 A "white" to "pink" noise filter

190

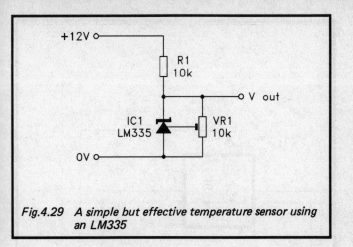

Fig.4.29 *A simple but effective temperature sensor using an LM335*

This gives a nominal operating frequency of 1100 hertz using the example values. R2 should be in the range 2k to 20k. C3 and C4 are the lowpass filter capacitor and output filter capacitor respectively. C4 should be at least double the value of C3. Making these values low enables the circuit to respond rapidly to the input tone, but making them too low will result in the circuit failing to lock-on properly. Low values for these components also give a very narrow locking range. The bandwidth is no more than a few percent even with C3 and C4 at relatively high values. The minimum input level for lock-on is about 15 millivolts r.m.s.

Finally, the circuit of Figure 4.32 is for a simple operational amplifier latch circuit. Taking the input high results in the output going high, and staying high even when the input is returned to the low state. S1 permits the output to be manually reset to the low state.

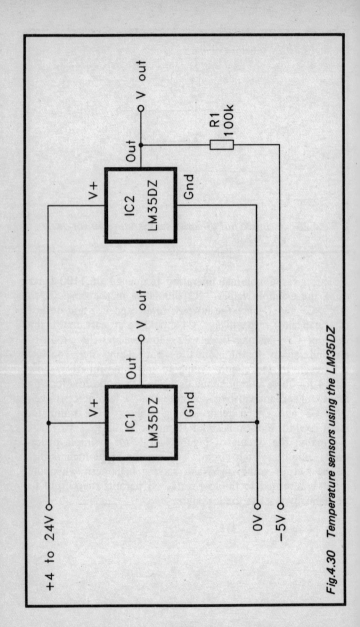

Fig.4.30 Temperature sensors using the LM35DZ

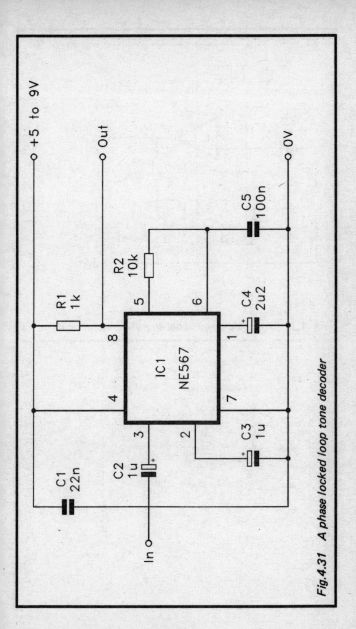

Fig.4.31 A phase locked loop tone decoder

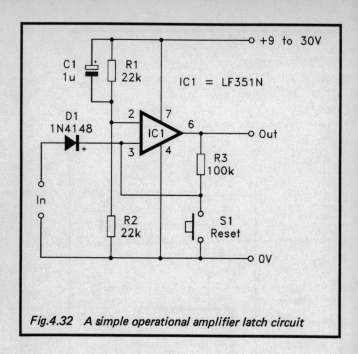

Fig.4.32   A simple operational amplifier latch circuit

Index of Circuit Figures

Index

Notes

Notes

Notes

Please note following is a list of other titles that are available in our range of Radio, Electronics and Computer books.

These should be available from all good Booksellers, Radio Component Dealers and Mail Order Companies.

However, should you experience difficulty in obtaining any title in your area, then please write directly to the Publisher enclosing payment to cover the cost of the book plus adequate postage.

If you would like a complete catalogue of our entire range of Radio, Electronics and Computer Books then please send a Stamped Addressed Envelope to:

BERNARD BABANI (publishing) LTD
THE GRAMPIANS
SHEPHERDS BUSH ROAD
LONDON W6 7NF
ENGLAND